The Gemini Man

The
Gemini Man

Susan Kelly

Walker and Company
New York

First published in the United States of America in 1985 by the Walker
Publishing Company, Inc.

Published simultaneously in Canada by John Wiley & Sons Canada,
Limited, Rexdale, Ontario.

Library of Congress Cataloging in Publication Data

Kelly, Susan.
  The Gemini man.

  I. Title.
PS3561.E39715G4 1985   813'.54   84–25703
ISBN 0-8027-5613-1

Book Design by Teresa M. Carboni

Printed in the United States of America

10 9 8 7 6 5 4 3 2 1

1

IT WAS AN extraordinarily cold night, even for November in Massachusetts.

Shivering, I stood on the front steps of my apartment building, rummaging in my shoulder bag for my keycase. It didn't seem to be there. Everything else I could conceivably need was—wallet, coin purse, comb, address book, lipstick, pens, pencils, checkbook, and compact. No keycase, though. I stabbed my finger on a stiletto-sharp pencil point and swore, more at my own stupidity than at the injury. The night would be a long one if I had to spend it camped on the porch.

I tried the door hopefully. Sometimes the dimwit who lived upstairs from me forgot to close it tightly behind him when he went in and out, and the lock didn't catch.

Apparently he'd remembered to do so tonight. Or someone else had shut the door after him. Just my luck.

I was on the verge of alienating my landlord by ringing his bell and dragging him away from his ritual contemplation of *The Jeffersons* when I recollected that I'd dropped the keycase into my coat pocket as I was leaving the restaurant a half-hour earlier. So I'd have it handy, of course. Shaking my head, I fished the keys out and unlocked the front door.

The foyer was wonderfully warm and bright. As I went up the stairs to my apartment I reflected how much nicer this place was than the one I'd lived in up until three weeks ago. Not that the old place had been a roach hotel or a firetrap. But it *had* been a bit on the small and rundown side. And I hadn't liked sharing the kitchen with the fat, elderly brown mouse who lived under the stove and sneered at traps, poison, my dog, and a couple of cats I'd borrowed in a fruitless attempt to get rid of him.

The new place had only three rooms, same as the old, but they were large, light, airy, and featured such amenities as built-in bookcases and polished hardwood floors. The living room had a bay window and a fireplace that worked without smoking up the entire building. The kitchen had a small pantry off it. And *no* mouse.

The building itself was three stories, with two apartments on each floor.

Above me were an elderly widow and the airhead who couldn't (usually) remember to close doors properly. The widow lived on Social Security and her husband's Cambridge Fire Department pension. The airhead lived on Quaaludes. He was doing a master's in social work at Boston University, or so I understood. Across the hall from me was another graduate student, a young woman in the psychology department at Harvard. Below were the landlord and a young married couple who operated a consulting firm in Brookline. What they consulted on or about, I didn't know.

But they were nice people, pleasant and quiet. Even the airhead was a vast improvement over some neighbors I'd had.

I let myself into my living room and snapped on the overhead light, feeling the same proprietorial pleasure I always did on entering the place. It needed more furniture, but the room was beginning to take shape. I'd finally gotten around to getting the books on the shelves and the pictures on the walls. The Mexican rug was a bright multicolored rectangle on the floor. Not half bad. I walked to the center of the room and turned around slowly, inspecting everything. About what you'd expect for a thirty-three-year-old unmarried ex-English professor making a haphazard but reasonable living as a free-lance writer.

Lucy, my runt chocolate Lab/weimaraner cross, emerged from the bedroom and trotted over to me, her tail wagging. I gave her a pat on the head, hung up my coat, and went into the kitchen to make myself a cup of tea.

I was getting the milk from the refrigerator when it occurred to me that Sunday night was garbage night in my part of Cambridge. Well, garbage eve, actually. The collection was the following morning. You could put your trash out Sunday night or get up at six A.M. Monday and do it then. As far as I was concerned, there was only one choice. I put the carton of milk on the counter and got a twist-tie for the trash bag from the cabinet next to the stove.

I *hate* getting up early, especially to do something as idiotic as put out garbage. That's one reason why I don't have what a lawyer friend of mine calls a "real" job. There are other reasons, too, but they have to do with temperament and education and opportunity rather than indolence.

I got all the trash assembled in a single plastic bag, slung it over my shoulder like a Bowery Santa's sack, and started for the door. When I got there, I patted my hip pocket to make sure I had my key. I *learn* from my mistakes.

I was closing the door behind me when I heard a noise like something falling at the other end of the corridor. I glanced automatically to my right.

2

My neighbor's door was open and light from her living room spilled out into the less well-illuminated hall.

"Joan?" I said.

There was no answer. I waited a few moments and then shrugged and picked up my sack of trash.

A man burst through the doorway of Joan's apartment, tripped over the threshold, and fell against the corridor wall.

"Hey," I said. For a few seconds we stared at each other. I had never seen him before. He certainly didn't live here. He was breathing heavily and his eyes had a sort of wide, glazed look. On the dark fabric of his coat and jeans there were darker, wet-looking stains. The muscles at the back of my neck tensed.

"Who the hell are you?" I said.

The man straightened up in a slow, painful motion and lurched toward me. As he approached, I could see that he was a lot younger than I'd thought at first. Barely out of his teens.

"Hey," I repeated. I reached out reflexively to grab his sleeve (not a bright move) and he shoved me aside. I stumbled and dropped the sack of trash. When it hit the floor the bag split and some of the contents spilled out onto the runner. A Styrofoam egg carton, an apple core, some lamb chop bones, and an empty fifth of vodka.

The guy in the stained clothes pounded down the stairs. A few seconds later I heard the front door open and slam shut.

"Jesus," I said, and shook my head. I looked back at the open door of the apartment across the way. "Joan?" I said, more loudly this time.

It was very quiet. I took a step in the direction of the other apartment and then halted. I wasn't quite sure what to do. The apartment seemed to be empty. On the other hand . . . weren't you just supposed to go somewhere safe and call the police if you suspected a break-in? At your own place or someone else's?

I walked the remaining ten or so feet down the corridor and poked my head cautiously through the open apartment door. The living room was brightly lit by the overhead fixture and by a lamp on the end table next to the sofa. I glanced to the left. The kitchen lights were on.

"I'm calling the cops," I announced firmly, for the benefit of whoever might be listening. My voice sounded odd in the stillness. I stepped into the room and looked around. It was difficult for me to say with any certainty, since I'd been in the apartment only once before this, but everything seemed okay. At least the stereo parts on the bookcase hadn't been disturbed. Nor had the portable electric typewriter on the coffee table. The whole place was, in fact, as orderly and spic-and-span as I'd noticed on my first visit. Maybe the guy I'd seen was a burglar who'd gotten nervous and taken off empty-handed when he'd realized someone was at home across the way.

I looked to the right. The bedroom door was slightly ajar. No light showed in the opening. I stood perfectly still, staring at it. If I pushed the door open, would someone else come rushing out at me? Some nut with a knife or a gun?

There was a muffled thump from the bedroom, as if a soft but heavy object had been dropped on the floor. I went rigid. What kind of moron was I to be standing here when I could be locked inside my own place, on the phone to the police?

After what seemed like the passage of several millennia, although it was probably only about thirty seconds, I heard another faint noise. A scratching sound, this time. The gap between the bedroom door and the jamb widened an inch or so and a furry, pale gray shape slid through the opening.

Joan's cat gave me a brief incurious look and stalked past me to the kitchen. I could feel my insides soften with relief.

I crossed over to the bedroom door and pushed it open with my fingertips. With my other hand I felt around on the inside wall for a light switch, located one, and snapped it on.

I honestly can't remember if I screamed or made no sound at all. Joan Stanley was home, and not about to get up and go anywhere under her own power. Ever. She was sprawled on her back diagonally across the bed, her arms outflung and her legs apart. The pink Qiana nightgown she was wearing had been pushed up around her shoulders. Her face was covered with blood. The sheet beneath her head was sodden with it.

I backed through the living room to the apartment door, my hands clamped over my mouth. I felt as if I'd been kicked in the chest by someone wearing lead-soled boots. My ears were buzzing, as if a swarm of wasps had somehow gotten trapped inside my skull. I leaned against the doorjamb for a moment, gagging into the palms of my hands. Then I groped my way back down the hall to my own place.

When I got inside, my legs gave and I half fell, half sank to the floor. I put my head between my knees and hugged myself, whimpering a little. The dog wandered over, gave me a concerned look, and nuzzled my hair.

With some effort, I raised my head and shook it several times. Then I pushed myself across the floor to the telephone table in the corner. I

4

grabbed the phone and dialed Jack's number. The first time around, my fingers were shaking so badly that I screwed it up and got a recording telling me that the number I'd reached had been disconnected. I tried again. This time I got the number right, but Jack didn't answer. I slammed the receiver back into the cradle, lifted it, and dialed his office number. Maybe he was working tonight.

"Criminal Investigation Division," a voice said.

"Is Lieutenant Lingemann in?" I asked faintly. "This is Elizabeth Connors."

"Just a minute." There was a click, a pause, another click, and then Jack's voice came on the line. "Hi."

"Jack," I said. "There's a—" My throat swelled up and I stopped speaking.

"What's wrong?" he said sharply.

I swallowed. "The girl who lives across the hall from me."

"What about her?"

I swallowed again, trying to dislodge the lump in my throat. "I think she's dead."

2

THE CAMBRIDGE POLICE Department consists of well over three hundred men and women. It seemed as if half of them spent the rest of the night in and out of Joan Stanley's apartment. And mine.

I was sitting at my kitchen table, drinking a cup of tea well laced with brandy and trying to focus on the questions Jack was asking me. There were quite a few. Some of them we'd gone over two or three times already.

"You got home at a quarter to ten," Jack said. "How long was it after that that you took the trash out?"

"Couldn't have been more than ten minutes," I said. "I came in, looked around, gave the dog a pat, hung up my coat, and went into the kitchen to make this." I gestured with the teacup.

"Okay. When you got inside the building, did you notice anything unusual?"

"Unusual like what?" I asked.

"You tell me," he said.

I thought for a moment. "No. Everything was fine. The hall lights were on, the outside door was locked."

"Hear anything?"

"No."

"All right, good. What about Joan's door? Was it open when you came upstairs?"

"I didn't notice." I looked at Jack. "Is that important?"

He shrugged. "I don't know."

"I really can't remember," I said. "I wasn't paying attention."

He nodded. "We'll get back to it. Describe the guy you saw coming out of the apartment."

"Again?" I said.

"Again," he said.

"Okay." I took a sip of tea and set the cup down. "He was young. Maybe twenty, twenty-one. About five-eight. Kind of skinny, I think. Not fat or big, anyway. Blond hair, medium long, down below his ears. Stringy-

6

looking. Bad skin. I don't know what color eyes. I'm pretty sure I'd know him, if I saw him again."

"Clothes?"

"Huh?"

"What was he wearing?"

"Oh. Jeans. And a pea coat. It had a big wet stain down the front. So did the jeans." I stopped speaking, glanced at Jack, and then said, "Oh, God."

"Oh, God what?"

"The mess on his clothes. Was that—?"

"I don't know," Jack said. "What else was there about him?"

I shivered. "Nothing. Maybe he was on some kind of drug. His eyes were sort of funny and shiny. What can I tell you? He was just a nondescript, grubby-looking kid."

"But you *would* recognize him?"

"Uh-huh."

"Good." Jack leaned back in his chair and gazed at me for several seconds, tapping the pen against his chin. I had a feeling I knew what he was going to say next. I was right.

"Liz, you did an incredibly stupid thing tonight."

I studied my cup. "I figured you'd get around to that."

"Why?"

I shrugged. "I don't know. I just went in there without thinking."

He shook his head. "You of all people ought to have more brains than to go barging into something like that. Suppose that guy hadn't been alone? Or he had a gun or something?"

"That occurred to me," I said. "Afterward."

"Yeah, well, it should have occurred to you right away. Jesus!"

A uniformed cop materialized in the doorway. I knew him vaguely; his name was something or other Franz.

"'Scuse me, Lieutenant," Franz said. "There's some people from the papers and the T.V. downstairs. You want to talk to them now?"

"No," Jack said. "But I suppose I have to. Thanks, Bernie."

The patrolman nodded and moved away. Jack got up, slipping his little notebook into the inside pocket of his jacket. He stood by the table for a moment, watching me intently. "Are you all right?" he said. "You look like you're going to faint."

"I won't," I said.

"Okay," he said. "I'll be back in a few minutes." He touched the top of my head lightly and left the kitchen.

7

I finished my brandied tea in two gulps and put the cup in the sink. Then I leaned against the counter and rubbed my temples slowly and methodically. The drink had arrested my shivering, but otherwise hadn't had much of a tranquilizing effect. My head felt light, and I was aware of a curious sense of dislocation, of being here and yet of not being here. Otherwise I was numb.

Hugging myself, although not from cold, I wandered into the living room. The door to the apartment was wide open. Through the entrance I could see a number of cops, some uniformed and some in plainclothes, moving up and down the hallway. Someone had picked up my spilled trash.

The photographer and the police artist who did crime scene sketches had come and gone. There were cops upstairs and downstairs talking to my neighbors. Probably six or seven others were out rousting the people in the surrounding houses, trying to find out if anyone but me had heard or seen anything.

A year and a half of being with Jack had given me a good idea of what was happening around me tonight.

I went over to the bay window and looked down at the street. There were five police cruisers, blue lights flashing, pulled up haphazardly to the curb. An ambulance, its rear doors open and waiting. A light-colored van, the Channel Five logo vivid on its side. And a lot of people milling around on the fringes with that aimless yet avidly curious look that spectators at a disaster or accident always have. I leaned against the windowsill, watching them. The sense of dislocation deepened.

There were footsteps in the doorway and I glanced over that way. Jack came into the room, accompanied by a middle-sized, stocky man in a navy blue blazer and gray polyester slacks. The man's dark hair looked as if it had just been blow-dried by a professional stylist. In the open collar of his shirt I could see a gold chain. He carried a bulky-looking black kit bag in his left hand.

"Liz," Jack said. "This is Detective Capuano."

"How do you do?" I said to the dark-haired man.

Capuano smiled. "Hi, Liz."

"Bobby's a fingerprint artist," Jack said. "He's going to take yours."

Startled, I looked from Capuano to Jack and back again. "What for?"

"Eliminate them," Capuano said. "From the others in there." He nodded once in the direction of Joan Stanley's apartment.

"Oh," I said. "Well, I only touched the bedroom door and the light switch."

Capuano smiled as if I'd said something extraordinarily clever and sat down on the couch. He opened the black kit and took from it a flat metal object that looked like a stamp pad. I glanced at Jack. He nodded slightly. I sat down next to Capuano. He smiled at me again, briefly, flipped open the stamp pad, and said, "This stuff washes off easy."

"I feel as if *I'm* the one who committed the crime," I said.

Capuano's movements were neat and economical. The whole process couldn't have taken more than three minutes. When he'd finished, Capuano snapped the stamp pad shut and dropped it in the black kit. "All done," he said. "You can wash off now."

I went into the bathroom and scrubbed the ink or whatever from my fingertips. Capuano was right; it came off easily. I dried my hands and went back to the living room. Capuano had left. Jack was standing by the fireplace. He hadn't taken off his sheepskin jacket.

"Well," I said.

"We have to talk some more," he said.

"What else can I tell you?" I asked.

"Whatever you know about Joan Stanley," he replied.

"Oh, boy," I said. "That's not much. I mean, I barely knew her. We were friendly, but we weren't friends or anything."

"Whatever you can tell me about her," Jack said. He shrugged out of his coat and draped it over the back of a chair. We sat down on the couch.

"Let me think for a second," I said.

"Think all you want." Jack took out his little notebook and opened it.

"Hmmm," I said. "Okay. Here's what I know about Joan Stanley. She's—she *was*, God—in the graduate school at Harvard. Doing a Ph.D. in psychology."

"What else?"

I deliberated a moment. "She told me she had some kind of part-time job in a counseling center."

"Which one?"

"That place over near Inman Square. The one that does crisis intervention and stuff like that. You know the place I'm talking about?"

He nodded. "What did she do there?"

"I'm not sure, exactly," I said. "I think she worked with rape victims. And high school kids with drug and sex problems. We never really talked about it much."

"Okay. What about Joan personally?"

I scratched my head. "What do you mean?"

He made a small circular gesture with his right hand. "What kind of a person was she?"

"Oh." I hesitated for a few seconds. "Nice. Quiet. She wasn't partying

9

all the time, if that's what you mean. I think she took her work pretty seriously."

"What about her friends?"

I shrugged. "What about them? I suppose she had people over once in a while. If she did, I never met them. There was a guy she went out with a lot."

"Did you ever meet *him*?"

I nodded. "Just once. His name's Richie. Richie Kearns. Oh, *God*."

"What's the matter?"

I looked at Jack. "Well, someone ought to tell him about—what happened. Before he reads about it in the paper tomorrow or sees it on the news, I mean."

"Somebody will," Jack said. "What do you know about him?"

"Nothing, really," I said. "I only met him just the once. He's at Harvard, too, but in the education department."

"How long were they going out?"

I held out my hands, palms up. "A while, I think. I had the impression it was sort of serious. I don't know if they were engaged or anything, but . . ." I let my voice trail off.

"Okay. What else?"

"That's it. I told you, Joan and I weren't close." I took a deep breath. "She seemed like a nice, bright, hardworking person."

"Uh-huh," Jack said. "Well, she didn't get killed because she was a nice, bright, hardworking person."

I scowled. "Oh, come," I said. "What are you suggesting, that she had some sort of sordid secret life? And it finally caught up with her?"

"I'm not suggesting anything," Jack said calmly. "I just try to find out what I have to know."

I looked at him for a moment and then nodded. "I'm sorry I can't be more of a help to you."

"You've been a help," he said.

The patrolman named Franz stuck his head in the doorway and said, "The medical examiner's here, Lieutenant."

"Okay," Jack said. He stood up, putting the notebook away. "Back in a while," he said to me.

Alone, I settled back on the couch and tried to recollect the various occasions on which I'd spoken to Joan Stanley over the past three weeks. There hadn't been many. The day I'd moved in, she'd come over and introduced herself. A few days later I'd gone to her apartment to borrow some Scotch tape, and we'd chatted for a few minutes then. We'd passed each other in the hall a number of times. She brought me some brownies she'd baked. I'd brought her some cornbread I'd baked. One night a week or so ago when I was on the way out to meet Jack, I'd run into Joan and Richie Kearns in the foyer, and she'd introduced me to him. The three of us had spoken briefly, pleasantries about weather and work.

And that was the extent of my relationship with Joan Stanley. As far as I was concerned, she was exactly as I'd described her to Jack. Quiet. Friendly. Intelligent seeming. Committed to her work.

So who would want to kill someone like that?

About twenty minutes had passed when I heard a bumping noise in the corridor. I got up and walked to the door and peered out. Two patrolmen were maneuvering a low, wheeled stretcher out of the doorway to Joan's apartment. On the stretcher was a long, white-blanketed bundle held in place by two straps. The two cops set their burden on the hallway floor and wheeled it past me. I stared at it as it rolled by.

Jack came up to me and put his hand on my shoulder.

"Where are they taking her?" I said.

"Funeral home," he replied. "They'll do an autopsy tomorrow."

I shivered.

"You all right?" Jack asked.

"Yes," I said.

"Feel like taking a ride to the station?"

I looked at him, puzzled. "Why?"

"I want you to look at some pictures."

"Oh," I said. "Okay. Sure." I glanced around me. "Anything's better than staying here alone tonight."

"Good," Jack said. He patted my shoulder. "Where's your coat?"

"I'll get it," I replied. "I have to check on the dog, anyway."

I went into the bedroom and called "Lucy" softly. There was a scrabbling noise from under the bed. A moment later the dog poked her muzzle through the fringe of the bedspread and gave me a wary look. She'd retreated under the bed when the first wave of cops had arrived earlier this evening. It was her favorite refuge. She showed no inclination to leave it now. I bent down and scratched her behind the ears.

"Behave yourself," I said. "I'll be back in a while."

Her tail thumped in reply.

I got my coat from the closet and rejoined Jack.

"All set?" he said.

"Uh-huh."

We were just starting down the stairs when a voice behind us said,

"Lieutenant?" We stopped and turned around. Patrolman Franz was walking toward us, carrying Joan's cat.

"What'll I do with it?" he said.

Jack looked startled. Then he shrugged. "Jesus, I don't know," he said. He glanced at me. "You know anyone who wants a cat?"

"Not me," I said. I thought for a moment. "Maybe you could take it upstairs and see if Mrs. Butler wants to keep it for a while. She likes cats."

Franz looked at Jack. Jack nodded.

"Okay," Franz said.

Jack reached out and scratched the cat under its chin. The cat purred and slitted its eyes.

"What's its name?" Jack asked.

"Cressida," I said.

"Cressida," he repeated. "Too bad you can't talk." He took his hand away and put it in his coat pocket. Franz and the cat started upstairs to Mrs. Butler's. Jack and I went down to the car.

3

FOR MOST OF the ride to the police station we were silent, each occupied with our own thoughts. Occasionally I glanced over at Jack. His face had a look of intense, frowning concentration. I'd seen that look before. I could almost hear his mind working.

It wasn't until we were getting out of the car at the police station parking lot that he spoke. "I hope you didn't think I was being unsympathetic, back there," he said. "I know what a shock it must have been for you. But . . ."

I shook my head. "It's okay," I said. "I didn't expect you to sit me on your knee and pat me on the head and tell me that everything was going to be fine."

"You'd have smacked me if I had," he said.

"Perhaps," I said.

He smiled a little and took my arm. Together we walked into the station. It was one o'clock in the morning, but the place looked like a subway platform at rush hour. Three uniformed cops at the desk. Others moving in and out of the ground floor offices. A group of people who looked like reporters standing around sipping coffee from Styrofoam cups. And oblivious to it all, an elderly man in a Red Sox cap and ankle-length tweed overcoat who huddled snoring at the end of one of the benches in the waiting area.

One of the reporter-looking guys spotted Jack through the crowd, set his cup on the desk, and moved toward us purposefully.

"Ah, shit," Jack murmured. He released my arm. "Go on up to my office. I'll be with you in a minute."

I did as I was told.

The office was open and brightly lit. I took off my coat and hung it on a rack in the corner. Then I settled in the chair across from Jack's desk to wait. I'd never looked at a mug book before. I wondered if I'd recognize any of the pictures. Or if there'd be one of the guy I'd seen coming out of Joan Stanley's apartment. If there were, it would simplify things enormously. Otherwise, they'd have to make a sketch of the guy based on my description of him. And that wouldn't tell them his name or where to find him.

Jack came into the office carrying two brown paperboard binders. He dropped them on the desk with a thud.

"Only two?" I said in surprise.

"Oh, no," he said. "There's plenty more where they came from. This is just the first round."

Bemused, I stared at the binders. They looked well-thumbed. "I may be here for a week," I said.

"There aren't that many," Jack said. He sat down behind the desk and raised his eyebrows at me. "Shall we get started? You want some coffee?"

I said yes to both questions.

"Tony," Jack yelled.

An astonishingly young-looking cop came to the door and said, "Yah?"

"Can you get us some coffee?" Jack asked.

"Just made a new pot," Tony said.

"Better than the last one, I hope," Jack said.

"Hey, I'm learning," Tony said.

I was on my third cup of coffee—Tony had a lot to learn—and fourth mug book when I saw a picture of the guy who'd been in Joan Stanley's apartment. I could feel my eyes widen.

"That's him," I said, pointing at the full-face photograph.

Jack had been leaning back in his chair, his hands clasped behind his head. At the sound of my voice he straightened up and put his hands on the desk. He looked at the picture very carefully and then at me. "You're sure?" he said.

"Absolutely," I said. "That's him. Who the hell is the little creep, anyway?" There was no name beneath the photograph, just a number and a date. "You know him?"

"Of course I know him," Jack said. He looked a little bit startled, though.

"What's the matter?" I said.

He shook his head. "Nothing." He got up and went to the door. "Hey, Sam."

A detective-sergeant I knew named Flaherty appeared in the doorway. I waved to him. He was a tall, thin guy with a slight stoop and graying red hair. Jack said something to him in a low voice. Flaherty frowned.

"Andy MacKenzie?" he said.

"Yeah, I know," Jack said. He glanced back at me. "But if that's who Liz said she saw, that's who she saw."

14

"You sure, doll?" Flaherty said.

"I'm positive," I said. "Who is this MacKenzie creature anyhow? The mayor's nephew?"

"Nothing like that," Jack said. He looked back at Flaherty and added, "Okay. Take Gil with you."

Flaherty nodded and walked away. Jack returned to the chair behind his desk.

"What now?" I said. I felt as if I were ready to tumble off my chair and pass out on the floor.

Jack gazed at me consideringly, biting his lower lip. "I'll get someone to take you home."

"Can't you?" I asked in surprise.

"No," he said. "I have work to do."

"Mmmm," I said. I stood up, swayed slightly, and grabbed the back of my chair to steady myself. Jack rose and came quickly around his desk and took me by the arm. I leaned against him.

"I'm sorry you had to go through that whole thing," he said. "You were a lot of help, if that's any consolation."

"I'm glad," I said. "I may go to sleep right here, though, standing up with my face in your shoulder."

"Come on," he said. "Let's find you a ride."

We started out of his office, me yawning mightily. Jack kept his arm around me. Probably he figured if he took it away I might fall down.

When we were in the lobby, I said, "Jack?"

"Yes?"

"May I ask you a question?"

"Of course."

I rubbed my eyes. "Joan," I said.

"What about Joan?"

I hesitated a moment and then said, "Was she raped?"

He nodded. "Yeah. It looks like it. We'll know better after the autopsy."

"God," I said. "That's awful."

"Being murdered's worse," Jack said. "Anyway—" he took a deep breath—"from what I could tell, she was probably already dead when he raped her."

4

PATROLMAN FRANZ DROVE me home in the chilly predawn. We didn't talk. He practically had to carry me from the car to my door. I thanked him for the ride, stumbled inside, let the dog out, let the dog in, peeled off my clothes, got into bed, and fell instantaneously into a deep and mercifully dreamless sleep. No visions of a bloody-faced Joan Stanley danced in my head.

The insistent clamor of the doorbell woke me at two-thirty Monday afternoon. I lay unmoving for a few seconds, debating whether to answer it. If the person at the door was someone selling magazines, I'd be furious at being dragged out of bed. On the other hand, it might be something important. While I was considering either alternative, the doorbell rang again. "Dammit," I muttered. I tossed back the bedcovers, got up, and padded barefoot to the front door. I punched the intercom button and said into the speaker "Yes?" in tones I hoped were as brusque as possible.

"It's me," Jack's voice said.

"Oh," I said. "Hi." I pushed the release button for the downstairs door, opened the apartment door, and went back to my room to put on a robe.

I was brushing my hair when Jack walked in. Lucy, tail churning, ran to the door to greet him. I followed more sedately, hairbrush in hand.

"I woke you," he said. "I'm sorry."

I shook my head. "Never mind. I had to get up one of these weeks, anyhow. And I'm glad to see you." I went over and gave him a kiss. "Just let me get cleaned up, though. I'll be with you in a minute."

He nodded and reached down to pat Lucy.

When I came out of the bathroom five minutes later I could smell coffee brewing. I walked into the kitchen. There were two places set at the table and Jack was standing at the stove, messing with a frying pan.

"My God," I said. "A short-order cook who makes house calls. Aren't you sweet?"

"Sweet," Jack said. "That's me. Sit down."

I did. "There's orange juice in the refrigerator."

"I know," he said. He put some scrambled eggs on my plate and on his. There was toast ready.

"No flowers?" I said. "No champagne cooling in a silver bucket?"

"You don't like champagne," he said.

"That's true," I said. Jack sat down and we started to eat.

"Did you just come from work?" I asked.

"Uh-huh."

I shook my head. "You must be exhausted."

He shrugged. If he was tired, he didn't show it. He looked good. He usually did. I studied him across the table. The way the light slanted in the kitchen window threw the bones in his face into prominence, giving his features an almost Indian cast. His hair and eyes were the same shade of light brown. In the summer, when he had a good tan, he was nearly monochromatic.

I thought he was wonderful-looking. I allow that I may be prejudiced.

I poured myself some coffee. "So how did things go with what's-his-name?" I asked. "Andy MacKenzie?"

"The way I thought they would," Jack said.

"Meaning what?"

Jack smiled a little. "He says he didn't kill Joan Stanley."

"So what else is new?" I said.

"I believe him," Jack said.

I put down the coffee pot and stared at him. "But—that *was* MacKenzie I saw coming out of Joan's apartment last night. I *know* it was."

"I'm not arguing with you."

"Well, what was he doing in there, then," I asked testily. "Borrowing a book?"

"Calm down."

"I *am* calm. But *really*, Jack."

He just looked at me, that same little smile playing around the corners of his mouth.

"Okay," I sighed. "Tell me why you don't think Andy MacKenzie killed Joan Stanley."

Jack shook his head slowly. "It's pathetic. MacKenzie was the janitor at that counseling place where Joan worked."

My eyebrows went up. "No kidding," I said. "So they knew each other, then."

"Yeah. I talked to the guy who's the assistant director there, a guy named Lewis, and what he told me was that MacKenzie had been giving them some trouble, lately."

"Surprise, surprise," I said. "What kind of trouble?" I held up my hand to forestall the reply. "No, let me guess. Something involving Joan?"

"Hey, you're smart," Jack said. "Uh-huh. Something involving Joan."

"Like what?"

"Lewis said MacKenzie had some kind of thing for her."

"A thing for her," I repeated. I poked at the eggs on my plate with my fork. "What kind of thing? You mean he had the hots for her?"

"Nicely put," Jack said. "The way you have with words, you must be a writer."

"Come on."

"Yeah. It was something like that, I guess. Anyway, it got to be a problem for Joan, after a while."

"How so?"

"Well, for one thing, MacKenzie started to hang around her office all the time. I mean *all* the time. She couldn't get any work done with him underfoot."

I put my elbows on the table and my chin in my hands. "So why didn't they just fire him? If he was that much of a nuisance?"

Jack shrugged. "They were in a bad position. This was the first job MacKenzie had that he'd been able to hang onto for more than a month. Plus he was in one of their rehabilitation programs."

"Wait a minute," I said. "Was MacKenzie on parole or something like that?"

Jack nodded.

"I assumed from his presence in your photo album that he'd had a few brushes with the law already," I said. "What's his problem?"

"Drugs."

"I'm not surprised," I said. "He looked as if he were on something when I saw him the other night. Go on."

"Lewis said that eventually MacKenzie started doing stuff like following Joan home. Calling her late at night. It was getting on her nerves."

"Yeah, I can imagine. How long had this been going on?"

"Since the end of September, Lewis said."

"God. So how did Joan deal with that?"

Jack shrugged again. "Lewis said he thought she handled it the wrong way."

"Why?"

"Ah, she was too nice to MacKenzie at first, I guess. She spent a lot of time talking to him about his problems, anyway."

I nodded. "So he took that as a sign of encouragement."

"Apparently."

"She really didn't have too much choice, though, when you think about it," I said. "I mean, she *was* a counselor. It was her job to talk to people like MacKenzie."

"Yes, but Lewis seems to think that she didn't make it clear enough to him that she was only interested in him from a—what? Professional standpoint?"

"Maybe she did," I said. "And MacKenzie was too dumb to take the hint."

"Could be," Jack said. "He's got the I.Q. of a turnip."

I giggled and then put my hand over my mouth. "I'm sorry. What a stupid time to laugh. Must be nerves or something. This isn't funny, is it?"

"Not especially," Jack said. He poured himself another half-cup of coffee. It was probably his fourteenth today.

"So what happened after that?" I asked.

"Nothing, really. It just went on in the same way."

"Oh, boy," I said. "And in all the time MacKenzie was trailing Joan around like a—a lovesick beagle, it never occurred to anyone that he might be dangerous?"

"Not that they told me."

I buttered myself another piece of toast. "There's something I don't understand."

Jack looked up from his plate. "What's that?"

"Well, if Andy was following Joan home all the time, and hanging around outside the building, how come I never saw him? Did Joan tell him to get lost?"

"Not in those words. But, yeah, Lewis said that she did finally talk to MacKenzie and tell him to cool it."

"Did he?"

"That's what MacKenzie says."

"And you believe him?" I said, trying not to sound too incredulous.

Jack shrugged. "He was here last night."

"Yes, he was. And that brings me back to my original question. What was he doing in Joan's apartment? Aside from beating her over the head and raping her?"

"He says he went to visit her. To talk to her. When he went in, he found her the way you did."

"Oh, for God's sake," I said. "That's ridiculous. If she was dead before he got here, how did he get in the building? He had a key?"

"He said the front door was open. He shut it behind him."

I frowned, puzzled. "How could that be?"

"That's what I'd like to find out."

Then it hit me. "Oh, God," I said. "The Quaalude Kid strikes again."

"What?"

I jerked a thumb at the ceiling. "The putz who lives upstairs. He never remembers to shut the downstairs door. It's open about half the time when I come in." I shook my head in disgust. "Jerk."

"Uh-huh," Jack said. "Tell me something else. Did Joan keep her apartment door unlocked?"

I thought for a moment. "I really don't know. Why?"

"Well, MacKenzie said it was open when he went in."

"Hmmm," I said. "That's possible, I suppose. I guess she might have left the door unlocked when she took the garbage down or something, and then not bothered to relock it. I know *I* do that, sometimes."

"You shouldn't," Jack said.

"Yeah, I know. In the future . . ."

"Keep your door locked," Jack said.

"I will." I nodded. "But getting back to the other thing . . . it *still* doesn't make sense. If MacKenzie didn't kill Joan, which I don't, by the way, for a minute believe, then that means that whoever *did* kill her didn't bother to lock the apartment door behind him when he left. Provided it was open to begin with."

"Why would he bother?" Jack said. "What difference would it make?"

I looked at him for a moment. "Okay," I said. "I'll go along with you on that one. But how did he get in the building?"

"Maybe the same way MacKenzie says *he* did. The outside door was unlocked when he came along."

I made a disbelieving face. "Isn't that a bit too coincidental?"

Jack shrugged. "Maybe. But you just told me the downstairs door is open half the time."

"Yes, I did, didn't I."

"So if it was somebody wandering around the street who found an open door—"

"And just went in on impulse?" I interrupted. "And found an unlocked apartment and walked in and saw Joan in her nightie and decided to . . .?"

"It happens," Jack said.

I shuddered. "Jesus, I *will* keep my door locked from now on."

Jack folded his arms and leaned back in his chair. "There's another possibility."

"What's that?"

20

"That she let whoever it was in."

"She knew—I mean, she was friendly with the person who did *that* to her?" I said, aghast. "My God, Jack, whoever it was was a—a—" I groped for the appropriate term. "A homicidal necrophiliac."

"So?"

"So she was friends with someone like that?"

He just looked at me.

"I know, I know," I said. "But . . ."

"But what?"

I sighed. "It must have been someone she knew pretty goddamned well. She was only wearing a nightgown."

"Uh-huh."

"There's no chance it was someone who broke in, is there?"

"I doubt it. There were no signs of forced entry."

"Boy," I said. "What a mess."

"Uh-huh."

"And you don't think MacKenzie did it."

"No, I don't."

"Who, then?"

"That's what I'd like to find out."

We were quiet for a moment. Jack made himself another piece of toast. I poured the last of the coffee into my cup.

"Jack," I said. "Did MacKenzie tell you how long he was in Joan's place?"

"He *said* about fifteen minutes." Jack emphasized the word "said," giving it a sardonic inflection. "He's not too sure. He's not very bright about stuff like that."

"Fifteen minutes," I said. "Fifteen minutes? What was he doing in there?"

"Sitting on the bed with Joan."

"*What?*" I nearly dropped my coffee cup. "But why—what kind of freak is he, anyway?"

"He's not a freak, really," Jack said. "He's just a poor, stupid loser." Jack shook his head slowly. "He says he went in the bedroom, saw Joan lying there, went over, and tried to pick her up. When it dawned on him that she was dead, he just sat there with her head in his lap. He says."

"That *was* blood on his clothes, then," I said. "Ugh." I looked at Jack. "So why did he bolt, then?"

Jack smiled at me. "You scared him."

"*I* scared *him*?"

"Well, when you came in. He heard your door open and close and he got frightened."

"So that snapped him out of his trance and he ran."

"Something like that."

I turned this over in my mind. "It could have happened that way, I suppose," I said grudgingly.

"We'll see," Jack said. He pushed back his chair and started to get up.

I looked at him in some surprise. "Going so soon?"

"Yes. I just stopped by to see how you were."

I smiled. "Where are you off to now?"

He put his plate in the sink. "The funeral home."

"I'm sorry I asked," I said. "Do you have to watch the autopsy?"

He nodded.

"What fun," I said.

"Has to be done," he said.

"I know," I said. I went over to him and put my arms around his waist. "This isn't going to be one of the easy ones, is it?"

"Uh-uh."

I tilted my head and looked up at him. "Jack?"

"Yeah?"

"You still haven't told me why you don't think Andy killed Joan."

He was silent for a few seconds. Then he said, "There was a bite mark on Joan's left breast."

I flinched and made a face. "And?"

He sighed. "Well, whoever did it had a full set of lower front teeth."

"So?"

"Two of MacKenzie's are missing."

5

AFTER JACK LEFT, I got dressed and took Lucy for a walk. It was a fine day, very bright and not ferociously chilly, but I was less concerned with enjoying the weather than I was with sorting out my thoughts. My thoughts had mostly to do with Joan Stanley. And with whoever it was who'd killed her.

On Mount Auburn Street, I stopped at a small variety store and bought copies of both Boston papers. "COED SLAIN IN CAMBRIDGE APT.", the *Herald* screamed. The *Globe* was a bit more sedate with "CAMBRIDGE WOMAN MURDER VICTIM." Both stories were accompanied by what was obviously a college graduation photo of Joan, looking grave, earnest, and terribly young. As I looked at it the memory of what I'd seen last night sprang to my mind with unnerving force and clarity. I folded the papers and tucked them under my arm. Lucy tugged at her leash, impatient with the delay.

We walked down Ash Street and crossed Memorial Drive to the river. The banks of the Charles are maintained as parks, with wooden benches set up at intervals so you can sit and watch the crews from Harvard and B.U. take practice. The view from any angle, in any season, is always beautiful and sometimes spectacular.

I unhooked Lucy's leash and she galloped down to the water's edge to poke around in a tall clump of dead weeds. "Don't go far," I yelled after her, no doubt pointlessly. Then I found myself an unoccupied bench and settled down to read the papers.

The *Globe* story reported that yesterday evening the body of Joan Ellen Stanley, 24, a graduate student in psychology at Harvard, had been discovered by a neighbor who then called the police. According to Cambridge Police Detective-Lieutenant John Lingemann, Ms. Stanley's death appeared to have been caused by "massive laceration of the skull from multiple blows on the head by a sharp instrument, probably a hatchet or a claw hammer." There were some indications that the victim had been sexually assaulted. No weapon had been found in the apartment, nor was there any evidence of a struggle. Robbery did not appear to have been the motive for the slaying. A man seen running from Ms. Stanley's apartment was being held by police for questioning.

The *Herald* story was as vague on the subject of Joan's rape as was the *Globe* story. I didn't attribute this reticence to any delicacy or squeamishness on the part of either writer. Long before I'd met Jack, and started to get a worm's-eye view of police dealings with reporters, I'd known that the cops will always withhold certain information about a case even from crime writers they like and trust. Reporters know this. Most of them accept it. Freedom of the press isn't the issue here. Some nuts get ideas for the crimes they commit from newspaper stories. And while there are reporters who will do almost anything to get the facts on a nice, juicy murder, I have yet to meet one who wants a story of his or hers to end up as inspiration for a potential homicidal maniac.

In any case, an imitative crime can mess up a police investigation better than almost anything else I can think of. After a while, you have no way of knowing how many murderers you're contending with. There are Boston and Cambridge cops who are absolutely convinced that the Boston Strangler was really two people, neither of whom happened to be the guy who finally confessed to the crimes.

I refolded the papers and dropped them in a pile beside me on the bench.

No weapon yet to be found.

No signs of a struggle in Joan's apartment.

No evidence of a robbery.

And, if Andy MacKenzie wasn't it, no suspect.

Beautiful. A real mystery. And nobody hates mysteries worse than detectives. When things like this happened, I wondered if Jack regretted not becoming the history professor he'd once planned to be.

I stood up, leaving the papers on the bench for the edification of the next occupant, and called for Lucy. A moment later she emerged from a bank of defoliated bushes and steamed up to me, panting furiously.

"Have a nice time?" I asked. She jumped up and planted her forepaws on my thighs while I attached the leash clip to the metal ring on her collar.

On the walk back home, I thought more about the murder.

I could figure out two possible sequences of events for Sunday evening. The first was that Joan had let her murderer into the apartment, not suspecting, not having any reason to suspect, that there was any danger. Whoever it was killed her, raped her, and left. After that, my horse's-ass upstairs neighbor had gone out, neglecting in his usual pharmaceutically induced trance to shut the front door behind him. Then MacKenzie had happened by, spotted the open door, entered the building, gone up to Joan's place, found *that* open, and gone in to find what he'd found.

Or—the putz upstairs left the building, not shutting the front door. The killer came along, got in and upstairs to Joan's, surprised her, killed her, and took off. Then the putz might have come back and forgotten to shut the front door yet again. And following that, MacKenzie had turned up and done his thing.

Farfetched? Too dependent on a series of wild coincidences? Maybe. But a hell of a lot weirder crimes had depended on far more bizarre circumstances for their commission.

And besides, in the case of Joan's murder—what other explanations were there?

It was dark by the time I got back to my place. As I was unlocking the apartment door, I glanced automatically to the right, at the entrance to Joan's place. The door was shut and sealed now, of course. On it was a sign that read "CRIME SCENE. SEARCH AREA. STOP. NO ADMITTANCE BEYOND THIS POINT UNTIL SEARCH IS COMPLETED. CAMBRIDGE POLICE DEPARTMENT."

And that was what the life of a twenty-four-year-old graduate student had come down to, in the end. The bottom line, as the folks at the Harvard Business School might say.

I went into my apartment and shut the door firmly behind me. I was careful to make sure it was locked.

6

THE FOLLOWING EVENING, I met Jack for a very quick drink at a bar in Harvard Square. Well, I was the one who had the drink—a vodka martini. Jack had a club soda. He had to go back to work in half an hour.

When I arrived at the bar, Jack was sitting at a corner table for two, drinking his club soda and listening attentively to what a blond woman standing with her thighs pressed against the rim of the table top was saying to him. The blonde was wearing a very low-cut red satin blouse and black slacks. Tight black slacks. She was drinking something that looked like a piña colada.

A piña colada in November, for Christ's sake. Some people have absolutely no sense of proportion.

I paused for a moment in the bar entrance, watching Jack and the blonde chatting. She was maybe twenty, and pretty in a bland, baby-faced way. She was also obviously enchanted by Jack. Taking all this in, I could feel myself starting to smile. Women have a tendency to fall all over Jack. This doesn't bother me. Actually, I think it's kind of flattering.

The blonde laughed at something and put her hand on Jack's shoulder. Then she leaned down and whispered in his left ear. He shook his head in response, smiling a little. I decided it was time to move in on the action.

I walked over to the table, cleared my throat, and said, "Good evening."

Jack glanced up at me. Perhaps it was my imagination, but I could have sworn he looked relieved. "Liz," he said. The blonde took her hand from his shoulder and straightened up. She didn't look pleased to see me.

"Liz," Jack said. "This is Sandra." He gestured at the blonde.

"How do you do, Sandra?" I said.

"Hi," Sandra said. "You with him?" She pointed at Jack.

"I sure hope so," I said, grinning.

"Yeah, I figured," Sandra replied. "Shit. Why are all the nice ones taken?" She slurred the word "nice" and I realized that she was quite drunk.

"Say goodbye, Sandra," I said.

"Yeah, okay," Sandra replied. "Shit. G'bye."

"Have a nice day," I said.

"Yeah, sure," Sandra said. She backed unsteadily away from the table and merged with the crowd around the bar. I shook my head and sat down. Jack looked at me and burst out laughing.

"You handled that beautifully," Jack said.

"Sandra, huh?" I said. "She one of your undercover vice officers?"

"How'd you guess?" Jack asked, picking up his club soda.

"I have a good eye," I said. "Did you order *me* a drink? Or were you so bewitched by little Sandra that it slipped your mind?"

"Drink's on its way."

"Oh, well done." I threw my coat over my shoulders and onto the back of the chair. I rested my forearms on the table top and leaned forward a little. "So how's everything going?"

He shrugged.

"That good, huh?"

"You know how it is, cookie."

I nodded. "I read the papers yesterday afternoon. Were the stories accurate?"

"More or less."

"So tell me more. What happened with the autopsy? Is MacKenzie definitely off the hook?"

"Well, he didn't kill Joan, anyway."

The waitress brought me my drink. I sipped it and said, "His bite didn't match the mark on Joan?"

"Nope."

"What else?"

He let out a long breath. "They did a saliva test on the bite area. Whoever did it had type A blood. MacKenzie's is O." Jack said all this very softly, so that I had to lean even farther across the table to hear him. "Also, they found a foreign pubic hair in Joan's vagina. It didn't come from MacKenzie."

"Yuck," I said. "Go on."

He looked at me closely. "You really want to hear this?"

I stared back at him. "Sure. Why not?"

"Well, it might upset you, that's all."

"If it does, I'll let you know."

"Okay," he said. "She *was* raped. Probably more than once. She was—uh, pretty torn up inside."

I pulled back automatically and made a face. "I get the picture," I said. "You don't have to elaborate."

"I wasn't going to." He finished his drink and signaled the waitress for another. He looked at my glass and I shook my head.

"What else is there?" I said.

"Not a hell of a lot," Jack said. "One thing, though. I don't think Joan knew what hit her." He grimaced. "Jesus. I could have put that better, couldn't I?"

"I'm glad she didn't know," I said. "But how can you tell if she did or didn't?"

"Well, the blow that did the most damage came from behind. It probably knocked her out right away."

"So she couldn't have tried to fight off whoever it was."

"No," he said. The waitress came with his club soda. He waited till she was gone before he resumed speaking. "There wasn't any skin under her fingernails, which there probably would have been if she'd tried to scratch the guy."

I put my chin in my hand. "Go on."

"There weren't any blood splashes or smears on the walls or floor. She must have been hit while she was on the bed."

"How much did MacKenzie disturb things while he was in there?" I asked. "I mean, if he sat on the bed with her and tried to pick her up . . ."

Jack shrugged. "It's hard to say. Not much, I think. What he told us pretty much corresponded with what we found. Some of Joan's blood was in the shower drain."

"What?" I stared at him. "How . . . ?"

"The guy probably took a shower afterward."

"Jesus," I said, shaking my head. "That's the sickest thing you've told me so far."

"Not sick," Jack said. "Or at least, not stupid. He cleaned himself off. He must have been covered with blood."

"God," I said. "It gets weirder and weirder, doesn't it?" I finished my drink. "Did the medical examiner say when he thought she got killed?"

"Closest he can fix it is sometime between seven-thirty and when MacKenzie walked in."

"Why seven-thirty?"

"The old lady living upstairs from you says she saw Joan putting her garbage out around then."

"Oh. Did my other neighbors tell you anything?"

"No. Nobody saw anything, nobody heard anything."

"What about the putz?"

28

"The who?" Jack looked mystified.

"The clown who lives upstairs from me," I explained. "The one who never shuts doors. Remember?"

"Oh, yeah," Jack said. "Him. Yeah. We spoke."

"Did you get anything coherent out of him?"

"Not much. He said he was in and out of the building a couple of times between seven-thirty and nine-thirty."

"And left the damn downstairs door open every time, too, I bet," I said. "That fool."

"Uh-huh. Want another drink?"

I looked at the clock over the bar. "Don't you have to take off in another minute or so?"

"I can stick around for a quarter of an hour."

"Okay, then," I said. "But only if you join me."

He nodded and ordered another vodka martini and another club soda from the waitress.

"Prints," I said.

"What?"

"In Joan's apartment. Were there any fingerprints besides Joan's and mine?"

"Yeah. Three sets. One was MacKenzie's."

"Whose were the other two?"

He shrugged. "Don't know yet. We sent them to Washington."

"Is that unusual?"

"What, sending prints to the F.B.I. for identification? No. We do it all the time. Come on. You know that."

"No, no. I meant, was it unusual for you to only find five sets of prints in the apartment? That doesn't seem like a lot to me."

"No. There's nothing particularly odd about that. Maybe she didn't have much company. Anyway, the place was very clean, so a lot of prints wouldn't have accumulated. Joan must have spent half her time washing things down and dusting."

"I noticed that, too," I said. "Both times I was over there. The apartment was so neat." I sighed. "Well, maybe that'll be a break for you. I mean, not having four thousand sets of extraneous prints to contend with."

Jack shrugged. "We'll see."

I nodded. "I guess we will." I was silent for a moment, turning things over in my mind. "Jack?"

"Yes?"

"What do *you* think happened that night?"

He raised his eyebrows. "I think Joan was expecting the guy. She let him in, they went in the bedroom, he got undressed, and . . ."

"But who?" I said. "Who was it? According to you, she was probably sleeping with the guy who killed her. She was pretty involved with Richie Kearns." I leaned forward to emphasize what I was going to say next. "I met Kearns, Jack. Granted I don't know him, but he seemed like such a sweet, quiet guy, I can't believe—"

"I didn't say it was Kearns," Jack said. "I'd like to talk to him, though."

I stared at him in astonishment. "You mean you haven't already?"

"I haven't had the chance to."

"Why not?"

"I can't find him. He's not at his apartment. Nobody's seen him since Sunday afternoon."

7

JOAN STANLEY WAS buried Thursday morning, in her family's plot in a Congregationalist cemetery in Wellesley. I didn't go to the funeral. Jack did, along with two other Cambridge detectives who shot four reels of movie film of everyone who attended the service. Later they'd make still pictures from the movie frames and show them to the people who had known Joan well, in the hope that someone might spot a face in the crowd that didn't belong there.

Some murderers like to go to their victims' funerals.

As for me, I was trying to get back into my normal routine. Thursday morning I spent putting the finishing touches on a truly tedious article on condominium conversion. It was something I really hadn't enjoyed writing, which is unusual for me—I think composing a shopping list is fun. When I'd finished typing the last page, I re-read the whole thing one last time, shoved it into a manila envelope, and took it to the post office.

When I got back to my place, there was a dark-green Chevy Malibu parked alongside the curb in front of the house. I recognized it as one of the unmarked police department cars. As I watched, Sam Flaherty got out and walked around to the passenger side of the car. He opened the door and a woman climbed out, a woman about my age wearing a gray coat and dark glasses. Her face was pale and had the taut look of barely sustained composure.

She and Flaherty came up the steps behind me as I was unlocking the front door. Flaherty nodded to me, unsmiling, and turned a little to the woman beside him. "Mrs. Holland," he said. "This is one of Joan's neighbors. Liz"—he looked back at me—"Mrs. Holland is Joan's sister."

There was a little pause, during which the three of us stared at each other. I swallowed nervously. "Mrs. Holland," I said finally. "I'm so sorry."

The woman nodded and contrived a faint smile. She looked awful. The dark glasses did little to conceal the puffiness of her eyes. Her lips were cracked and colorless.

What do you say to the relative of a murder victim?

31

I opened the door and let Mrs. Holland precede me over the threshold. In the foyer she stopped and looked around vacantly.

"This is a nice building," she said. "Joan liked it." Then she started up the stairs. Her tread was leaden and mechanical.

I hung back and grabbed Flaherty by the sleeve of his jacket.

"Sam," I whispered. "Can I do anything? That woman is in very rough shape."

"Yeah, I know," Flaherty said. "Shock." He shook his head. "No. I can't think of anything. But thanks."

"Okay," I said. "If you change your mind, you know where I am." He nodded and gave me a pat on the shoulder.

I had climbed half the first flight of steps when Flaherty said, "Wait a minute."

I halted and looked back at him curiously.

"On second thought, maybe you better come with me," he said. "I think she might break down. If there's another woman there . . ." His voice trailed off and he shrugged.

"Sure," I said. We resumed climbing the stairs together. "Why's she here?" I asked, keeping my voice low.

"She wanted to pick up some of Joan's personal stuff," Flaherty said, in tones as soft as mine. "And we thought she might be able to take a look around and tell us if there was anything missing."

I frowned. "But didn't—I mean, I thought you had pretty much established that there wasn't any robbery."

Flaherty shrugged again. "Well, the place wasn't ransacked. We brought the girl's parents here Monday morning, and they said there wasn't anything missing, but they weren't in any shape to take a real careful look."

"No," I said. "I can't imagine that they would have been."

Mrs. Holland was standing before the entrance to Joan's apartment, gazing fixedly at the crime-scene sign on the door. "Excuse me, Mrs. Holland," Flaherty said gently. She moved a little to the side and he unlocked the door. I followed the two of them into the apartment.

The living room was dim and stuffy.

"It's very dark in here," Mrs. Holland said. She went to the window and pulled back the curtains. A flood of afternoon light spilled into the room. I peered around me. The coffee table and bookshelves were covered with a fine layer of dust. The sofa was pulled slightly away from the wall. Everything seemed minutely disheveled in the wake of the forensic team.

"Mrs. Holland," Flaherty said.

She turned to him.

He cleared his throat. "Ah—we were hoping that you could sort of, you know, take a look around and tell us if you noticed anything out of place. Or anything missing." I had never heard or seen Flaherty so uncomfortable.

Mrs. Holland just nodded.

"Would you like to start in this room?" Flaherty asked.

"Yes," Mrs. Holland said. "I think that would be a good idea." She set her handbag on the coffee table and began walking slowly around the room, every so often pausing to inspect a book or other small object. I leaned against the doorjamb, my arms folded, and watched her. Flaherty sat down on the couch and watched her. She was oblivious to us both.

After about five minutes, Mrs. Holland said, "Everything seems fine to me. I don't think there's anything missing, or anything here that shouldn't be." I marveled at the precision of her diction.

"Good," Flaherty said. He rose from the sofa. "Would you like to take a look at the other rooms?"

"Yes, certainly." She turned and faced Flaherty directly. "I suppose you would like me to check the bedroom. That was where it happened, wasn't it?"

I tensed a little.

"Yes, Mrs. Holland," Flaherty said. "We'd appreciate it."

She nodded and went to the bedroom door. Flaherty followed her, and so, with a distinct feeling of unease, did I. Maybe I had made a mistake in offering to be present while Mrs. Holland went through the apartment. As far as I could tell, all I was doing here was intruding on someone else's grief.

The bed had been stripped of its bloody sheets, of course, but the naked mattress still bore a large brownish stain. I glanced at it and averted my eyes. Mrs. Holland ignored it. "May I touch anything?" she said to Flaherty.

"Yes," he said. "Of course."

Mrs. Holland went to the dresser and pulled open the top drawer. She began riffling quickly through the contents. A pair of pale blue bikini underpants fell to the floor. I was going to retrieve them, but Flaherty stopped me with a single small sharp gesture. I leaned against the wall by the door, my hands behind my back.

Mrs. Holland took a small metal box from the dresser and opened it. "Joan's jewelry," she said. She reached into the box and removed a thin gold chain from which depended a heart-shaped locket. "My parents gave this to Joan when she was thirteen." She held the locket up and gazed at it for several seconds. I bit the inside of my lower lip.

With a small sigh, Mrs. Holland dropped the locket back into the jewelry case. She pressed the lid down on the box and set it carefully on the dresser. Then she moved across the room to a small bookcase crammed with looseleaf binders and psychology texts. She knelt down beside it and pulled out a black plastic notebook. I glanced over at Flaherty. He was following Mrs. Holland's movements very intently.

"The statue's gone," Mrs. Holland said abruptly. She straightened up, a faintly puzzled look on her face.

"What statue is that, Mrs. Holland?" Flaherty asked quickly.

"I gave it to Joan about four Christmases ago," Mrs. Holland said. "She always kept it on top of this bookcase. It was a reproduction of an African piece. Cast iron, I think. Very heavy. Maybe this high." She spread her hands apart about eighteen inches.

"What did it look like?" Flaherty said.

Mrs. Holland shook her head slightly. "It was a figure of a woman. In a turban. Very elongated."

"Was it mounted?" Flaherty asked.

Mrs. Holland looked thoughtful. "I think so. Yes. Yes, it was. On a flat metal base. The edges looked very sharp, I recall."

I took a deep breath and let it out slowly. There was a growing sick sensation in the pit of my stomach.

"Why would anyone want to steal something like that?" Mrs. Holland said. "It wasn't in the least bit valuable. I only paid about twenty dollars for it."

"Excuse me," I muttered. Flaherty shot me a sharp glance.

I pushed myself away from the wall and walked quickly out of the room. I didn't want to be around when Mrs. Holland figured out why the statue was gone.

34

8

"IT WAS SO awful, Jack," I said. "There was this poor zombie of a woman standing there wondering why somebody'd ripped off her Christmas present to her sister, and I mean, it was so *obvious* why the thing had been taken."

Jack shook his head, taking a bite of tuna sandwich. It was Friday afternoon, and we were sitting in his office, having a sort of picnic lunch catered by me. He didn't have the time to go out anyplace to eat. He almost never did.

"I really feel kind of guilty," I said. "I just took off and left Sam there with Mrs. Holland. And this was after I'd offered to hang around and help out in case she got hysterical or anything." I curled my lip. "Some great help, huh?"

"Don't worry about Sam," Jack said. "He can handle stuff like that. He's been doing it for twenty-five years."

"I know," I said. "But still . . . it was sort of cowardly of me to take off like that, don't you think?"

"Forget it," Jack advised. "It's not your fault. That really is a tough thing to deal with, a situation like that, if you're not used to it."

"Must not be all that easy even if you are," I said.

"No," he agreed. He finished his sandwich and pried the lid from a Styrofoam cup of coffee.

"You think the statue was the weapon?" I asked.

He raised his eyebrows. "Well, I haven't found it, have I? I couldn't say unless I saw it. But yeah, something that size and shape and weight could have caused the kind of damage that was done to Joan's head. Quite easily. And it was right there at hand."

"What significance does that have, I wonder?" I said.

"Hmmm?"

"Does the fact that the statue was just sitting there on the bookcase, available, mean that the guy got the idea to kill Joan only after he noticed it and realized what a good weapon it would make?"

Jack shrugged. "It could, I suppose. But I have the feeling he didn't kill her on impulse. The whole thing was too carefully worked out for that."

"Oh?"

"Sure. The way he cleaned up after himself. And if he had been sleeping with Joan for a while, he'd have known the layout of her bedroom, so he'd have known that the perfect weapon was sitting right there on the bookcase. He wouldn't have had to bring anything with him."

"So you don't think it was a spur-of-the-moment thing, then?"

"Nope. I think he knew what he was going to do long before he got to her place."

"Wow," I said. I sipped my coffee. "Okay, then. Your working hypothesis is that Joan was killed by somebody she knew and presumably trusted and who had planned the whole business out down to the last detail beforehand."

"You could put it that way," he said, smiling.

"What are you grinning at?" I asked suspiciously. "What's so funny?"

"Nothing. I just like your use of the word 'hypothesis,' that's all."

"What's wrong with it?" I demanded. "It's a perfectly good word."

"Did I say it wasn't? Jesus, are you touchy."

"Well, I don't like being humored. Especially by you."

He rolled his eyes at the ceiling and shook his head slowly. "Christ. All I meant was that the word 'hypothesis' has such a good scientific ring to it. Makes me feel as if I know what I'm doing."

"Don't you?"

"Oh, hell, no. I just grab at straws."

I laughed and tossed my empty coffee cup into the wastebasket. Jack leaned back in his chair and put his feet on the desk. His tie was loosened and he looked totally relaxed, almost somnolent. It was a technique he'd cultivated after the pressure of the job had started giving him chest pains.

"We got the prints back from Washington," he said presently.

"*Ohhhh.*" I widened my eyes. "Whose were they?"

"Kearns's," Jack said. "And a guy named Christopher Bingham."

"Who's Christopher Bingham?" I asked.

"Guy in the psych department at Harvard," Jack said. "One of Joan's professors."

"Uh-huh. Have you talked to him?"

"Of course."

I nodded. "I take it Richie Kearns hasn't turned up yet."

"Nope."

"Any idea where he might be?"

"If I had any idea where he might be, I'd go there and get him."

"Yeah, you would. So how come the F.B.I. had his and Bingham's prints? Was either one of them ever arrested?"

"Not that I know of. But they were both in the army. Bingham in Germany and Kearns in Vietnam."

"So," I said. "Joan was friendly with one of her professors, then."

"Apparently. Do you think that's odd?"

"Not at all," I said. "I was bosom buddies with *my* dissertation adviser. He and his wife used to have me over for dinner all the time. I think they were afraid I'd starve to death in the middle of chapter five if they didn't feed me. My fellowship wasn't all that lavish."

Jack smiled. "Well, I gather that Joan's relationship with Bingham was a little less—uh, wholesome than the kind of thing you're describing."

I looked at him. "Oh? How so?"

"What I heard was that he and Joan were having an affair."

"Good God," I said. "Did Bingham tell you this himself?"

"No."

"Well, then, where'd you get it from?"

"Two different people. Some friends of Joan. Two other grad students named Lisa Waite and Robin Peterson. According to them, everybody in the psych department knew, or was guessing, that something was going on between Joan and Bingham."

"Jesus H. Christ," I said, scratching my head. "Is Bingham married?"

"Uh-huh. With three kids."

"God," I said. I was surprised at how shocked I was. "How the hell many guys was Joan sleeping with?"

Jack shrugged.

"Okay," I said. "Setting *that* point aside for the moment, did Kearns know about Bingham?"

"Well, from what Lisa Waite told me, he didn't up until recently."

"How'd he find out?"

"Joan told him. At least, she told Lisa Waite that she was going to tell him."

"But . . . I was under the impression that Joan was sort of engaged to Kearns."

"Yeah, well, Kearns seems to have been under the same impression. Or so I've been told."

"God," I said softly. "That's really something." I shook my head. "So was this business with Bingham just casual?"

"Well, the Waite woman told me it had been going on for about four or five months."

"And?"

"According to her, Joan had been putting some pressure on Bingham for him to leave his wife. Bingham apparently wasn't too crazy about that idea."

"I see," I said. "And did you confront him with all this?"

"Oh, my, yes."

"And?"

"Well, he denied it. He said that yes, he'd been friendly with Joan, and that yes, he'd been in her apartment once or twice, but only to deliver some work to her—she was his teaching assistant, and I guess she graded papers for him—but beyond that, he says there was absolutely nothing going on between them."

"Wow," I said. "So who do you believe? Lisa Waite and—what was the other one's name?"

"Robin Peterson."

"Yes, right. So who do you believe? Them or Bingham?"

He grinned at me. "Who do you think?"

"Silly question," I said. "Tell me—what was dear old Professor Bingham doing last Sunday evening?"

"Why do you ask?"

"Oh, no special reason. It just occurred to me that a married guy with a reputation to maintain in the academic community might feel a little bit harried if a woman student he'd been sleeping with started bugging him about divorcing his wife."

"What a suspicious mind you have," Jack said. "Well, Bingham *says* he was in the Science Center Library from about seven till closing time. Working out some statistical data for an article he's writing. He showed me the notes."

"What's closing time at the Science Center Library?"

"On Sundays? Midnight."

"Uh-huh. Did anyone see Bingham there?"

"He says he was in the stacks practically the entire time. He didn't notice anyone in his section, and he doesn't think there's any reason why anyone would have noticed him. Or remember if they did. He could be right."

"That's true," I said. I thought for a moment. "Jack, I've been in the Science Center Library. It only has one exit."

"Yes?"

"Well, when you leave, the guards always check your bags and brief-

38

cases to make sure you're not toddling off with last year's run of *The Bulletin of the Atomic Scientists* or like that."

"I know that, cookie."

"So? Assuming Bingham didn't parachute out a window or shinny down a drainpipe, he must have left by the legitimate exit."

"Makes sense," Jack agreed. I looked at him sharply. His face was bland and innocent as a toddler's.

"So did you check with the guard who was on duty Sunday night? Ask him if he remembered seeing Bingham?"

"No," Jack said, in tones of exaggerated astonishment. "That never once occurred to me. Son of a bitch. I'll get Sam on it right away."

I could feel my face turning red. Jack laughed.

"Yes," he said. "In answer to your question, yes. I *did* check with the guard. He doesn't remember seeing Bingham."

I perked up. "Well, then . . ."

Jack shook his head. "It's not that simple. There were a couple of hundred people in the library Sunday night. And most of them waited till they got kicked out at closing time to leave. There was a big stampede at the exit. The guard says he checked out about a hundred and fifty people between eleven-forty-five and midnight. He doesn't remember individual faces. Christ, he'd've let Bigfoot through the checkpoint provided he wasn't trying to steal a book."

"Shit," I muttered.

"Don't take it so hard," Jack said.

I smiled at him. "I guess I was jumping to conclusions."

"Maybe. Maybe not. Sometimes things are exactly that easy. Other times they aren't. In this business, you never know."

I nodded. "It *is* sort of complicated, isn't it? Boy. A woman is more or less engaged to one guy. She tells him that she's been sleeping with yet another guy for four or five months. Then she gets murdered. The fiancé disappears. The other guy can't really account for his time the night she got killed." I blinked. "So what do you do? Flip a coin? Heads it's Kearns, tails it's Bingham?"

"You're forgetting something," Jack said.

"I am?"

"Uh-huh." He clasped his hands behind his head. "The place where Joan worked."

"What about it?"

He smiled. "Who were her clientele, besides Andy MacKenzie?"

I stared at him. "At a counseling center? A bunch of druggies and flakes."

"Exactly."

"And Joan *did* get murdered in a very flaky way."

"Yup."

9

I LEFT THE police station about ten minutes later. Jack had to get back to work, and there seemed little point in my hanging around his office impeding progress or obstructing justice or whatever. In any case, I'd probably be seeing him later in the evening.

I walked slowly down Western Avenue toward Central Square, mulling over what I'd just learned about Joan Stanley. The fact that she'd been messing around with one of her professors didn't bother me. What bothered me was that she'd been doing it while she was supposed to have been involved with Richie Kearns. How serious, then, had she been about either guy? According to her friends, she'd been virtually engaged to Richie Kearns. But, according to those same friends, she'd also been pressuring Bingham for a serious commitment from *him*. Did that mean that she was in love with both men and unable to make up her mind which one she really wanted to be with? Or did it only mean that she was playing both ends against the middle?

The situation was one I couldn't understand, because I couldn't imagine myself being in it. In the year and a half I'd spent with Jack, I hadn't even gone out with another man, much less slept with one. It wasn't a question of fidelity or morality. I simply had no desire to be with anyone else. I knew lots of men—attractive ones, too—that I liked and was friendly with, but beyond that . . . nothing.

So what had it been with Joan Stanley, then? Had she thought that she'd loved Kearns, then gotten involved with Bingham and realized that what she felt for Bingham was a lot stronger than what she'd felt for Kearns? *That* I could see happening. But if such were the case—why had she let things drag on so long with Kearns?

The older I get, and the more I hear and see, the less fathomable human motivation becomes to me. Jack would say it's a waste of time to sit around trying to comprehend the incomprehensible. I'm sure he's right.

In any case, Joan Stanley's motives, intentions, hopes, whatever they may have been, were buried with her in that plot in Wellesley, and thus beyond *anyone's* reckoning.

Better to concentrate on the things that could be known or found out. Such as who had killed Joan Stanley, and why. Not that either one of those would be all that easy to figure.

I reached the intersection of Massachusetts and Western Avenues. The digital clock on the bank across the street read two-fifteen. I had an entire afternoon ahead of me to fill up as I pleased. What better way to spend it than by trying to find out the answers to the questions that had begun bugging me about this whole Joan Stanley business?

First stop: the counseling center where Joan had worked.

If Central Square is police headquarters, City Hall, the main post office, and the Division of Employment Security, Inman Square is bars. This isn't to suggest that Central hasn't lots of drinking establishments. It does. But as far as I can see, the *raison d'être* for Inman Square is the dispensation and consumption of booze. And music. For some reason, all the jazz clubs in Cambridge end up in Inman Square. Three of them in a two-block area, by my last count.

But I wasn't in Inman Square to boogie, I was there to look for the crisis and counseling center. I found it between a boarded-up five-and-ten and a boarded-up shoe repair place. The structure the center occupied looked as if it had once housed a neighborhood supermarket, the kind that are being squeezed out of existence by the grocery chains. The plate glass windows had been inexpertly painted over a dull green. The painter had left about two feet of space clear at the top to let in light. On the door there was a hand-lettered cardboard sign listing the days and hours the center was open. A festive note was furnished by the empty pint bottle of domestic port someone had left on one of the window ledges.

Judging by its exterior, the Inman Square Crisis and Counseling Center wasn't rolling in big government-grant bucks. In fact it looked as if it were barely meeting the overhead. I pushed open the door.

The interior of the place was about as prepossessing as the exterior. The walls were that dreadful institutional dun color, and peeling in spots. The floor was beige-speckled linoleum. Beneath the windows on either side of me were rows of molded plastic chairs, presumably where you sat while waiting to see your counselor. One of the chairs was occupied by a fat woman in a blue coat who sat absolutely motionless, her hands folded in her lap and her eyes fixed on the wall opposite her. The rest of the room had been partitioned off into minuscule offices. Through the open door of one I could see a metal desk and two chairs. In the space before me was another desk at which sat a young, frizzy-haired woman laboriously bashing away at an elderly Remington manual. On the desk was a plastic sign that said RECEPTIONIST. A few inches away from the sign was a small ceramic statue of a wistful-looking gnome-like creature, the kind you can buy in the really cheapo gift and souvenir shops. The gnome was mounted on a pedestal that bore the legend "I NEED WOTS OF WUVE." Peering at it, I made myself a bet that in at least one of the cubbyholes, someone would have tacked up a poster that read "TODAY IS THE FIRST DAY OF THE REST OF YOUR LIFE."

The receptionist looked up from her typing and said, "Can I help you?" Her accent was purest Cambridgeport.

I smiled and introduced myself. "Is the director of the center in?"

Without getting up, or even turning her head, the receptionist yelled, "Peter." Apparently the staff of the Inman Square Crisis and Counseling Center didn't stand on ceremony.

A moment later a tall, dark-haired man emerged from one of the cubbyholes. "What is it, Diane?"

"Somebody here to see you," the receptionist replied. She jerked her head at me and went back to her typing. The dark-haired man gave me a questioning look.

"Hello," I said. "Are you the director?"

"Assistant director," he corrected. "Peter Lewis."

I recalled Jack mentioning someone by that name. I skirted the receptionist's desk and walked toward Lewis, my hand extended. "My name is Elizabeth Connors."

Lewis took my hand and we shook. "Nice to meet you," he said, smiling. "Is there something we can do for you?"

Now came the tricky part. It had occurred to me during the walk to Inman Square that, being neither reporter nor cop, I could hardly just burst into the counseling center and start demanding the lowdown on Joan Stanley. And the concerned-neighbor-of-the-victim routine would only get me so far. I knew from experience that unless I had some legitimate reason to be asking for information, nobody would give me any.

I could, of course, represent myself as a free-lance writer doing a story on the case for one of the local magazines.

The more I thought about it, the better the idea seemed to me—and not just as an excuse to get Joan's co-workers to open up about her, either. The case *would* make a fine story. On the surface a fairly straightforward account of a particularly brutal murder, but underneath, something far more complex and ambiguous. I knew an editor who would love it.

And, I realized as I walked, it was a story I really wanted to do. A lot more interesting than the usual crap I wrote about. Certainly more important.

I returned Lewis's smile. "I hope you *can* help me," I said. "I'm here about Joan Stanley."

The receptionist stopped typing. Lewis's expression became a trifle less cordial. "Are you from the police?" he asked. His tone wasn't quite as warm as it had been before.

"No," I said. "I'm not. I was Joan's neighbor."

"Oh," Lewis said. He paused a moment, frowning slightly, as if trying to remember something. "Her neighbor? Were you the person who discovered the . . . who found her?"

I nodded.

"God," Lewis said, shaking his head. "That's terrible." He glanced over his shoulder and gestured at one of the cubbyholes. "Look, let's talk in my office."

Lewis's office was cramped and untidy. The top of the desk was stacked with papers. One of the piles was weighted down with a cardboard cup of half-drunk coffee. The cream in it had congealed. Appetizing. Against one wall was a packing-crate bookcase that had been painted a vivid green. The books in it had titles like *Deviance*, *The Family Therapist*, *Studies in Social Psychology*, *Drugs and Alcohol*, *The Pathology of the Sexual Offender*, and *The Disturbed Adolescent: Case Studies*. Over the bookcase were framed diplomas from Stanford and Indiana. The Indiana diploma hung slightly askew. Lewis had a B.A. in psychology, I noticed, and a master's in psychiatric social work.

Lewis swept a pile of papers off the spare chair and said, "Sit down, please." I did, with a smile of thanks. He leaned against the corner of his desk and folded his arms.

"So what can I do for you?" he asked. The friendliness was back in his voice.

"Well, as I told you, I'd like to find out whatever you can tell me about Joan Stanley."

"Why?" There was no hostility in the question, just curiosity.

"I'm a writer," I said. "And I'm doing a story on her."

"I see," Lewis said. "What newspaper do you work for?"

"No newspaper," I said. "I do mostly free-lance." In the interest of convenience—my convenience—I decided to stretch the truth a little. "*This* article I've been asked to do for *Cambridge Monthly*. Here, I can show you some identification, if you'd like." I reached for my handbag.

"That's okay," Lewis said, waving away my offer. "I believe you. But"—he stopped and scratched the side of his nose—"I'm a little puzzled why *Cambridge Monthly* would be wanting an article on Joan."

"Not so much on her," I replied, "as on the murder itself."

"Uh-huh," Lewis said. He sighed. "Look, I don't, God knows, mean to sound callous about what happened to Joan. But there are *lots* of murders. I can understand your interest in this one, but why should *Cambridge Monthly* care about it?"

"Well," I lied, "my editor is very concerned about the rise in violent crime. I think he sees what happened to Joan as sort of symptomatic of what's going on in society in general." I was glad Jack wasn't listening to this crap. I'd never hear the end of it. "Anyway," I continued, "the case *is* an unusual one. There are aspects of it that have the police puzzled." That much was true, at least.

Lewis gave me a considering look. I waited hopefully. Several seconds passed. Through the open door I could hear Diane's typewriter rattling away. "Okay," Lewis said finally. "I'll tell you what I can. But—" he warned, "that's not much."

I smiled. "Whatever you can give me, I'll appreciate."

Lewis reached over, pulled the other chair out from the desk, and dropped into it. He stretched out his legs, crossing them at the ankles, and rested his elbows on the arms of the chair. "So?" he said, smiling. He had an engaging manner, direct and good-natured. I felt a little twinge of guilt at deceiving him, even if only slightly. Tough shit.

"So," I echoed. "Tell me something about Joan. What kind of work did she do here?"

"Same as we all do," Lewis replied.

"Oh?" I reached into my handbag and extracted a small notebook and pen. I flipped open the notebook and rested it on my knee. Professional. "What is it you all do?"

"Individual counseling," Lewis replied. "Couples counseling, group therapy, family therapy, crisis intervention, psychological testing, and psychiatric evaluation. We have a child abuse treatment team."

"Uh-huh," I said, scribbling wildly in my notebook. "How many on your staff?"

"Oh, boy," Lewis said. "It's hard to keep track, we grow so fast. Let's see. There's the director, Sheldon Lederer. He's a psychiatrist. We have four full-time psychologists, seven psychiatric social workers, and about six post-doctoral or grad students like Joan. And some community volunteers we've trained in counseling."

"Graduate students like Joan," I said. "Are they limited to certain duties? I mean, they're not licensed psychologists or social workers. Can they only counsel certain types of patients?"

"We try to avoid the term 'patient,'" Lewis said. "We prefer to call the people who come to us our clients. But no, Joan didn't, the other students don't, have any restrictions placed on them in terms of the kind of clients they can see. They work under supervision, that's all. Joan herself dealt with a varied group. She was working with a rape victim, I remember, and with some alcohol and drug dependency cases."

"Like Andy MacKenzie," I said.

"Oh," Lewis said. "You know about him."

"Well," I said wryly. "I saw him running out of Joan's apartment that night. I picked him out of a police mug book."

"Jesus, that's right," Lewis said. He gave me a sympathetic look. "Must have been a hell of an experience for you. Going in there and seeing that . . ."

"Yes," I said slowly. "I guess it was. I try not to think about that part too much."

"Is that why you agreed to write about it?" Lewis asked.

"What?" I was a little disoriented by the suddenness of the question.

Lewis smiled. "Does writing about what happened, dealing with it as if it were an intellectual problem—does that help you to put it in some kind of perspective?"

I shook my head. "I don't know. I hadn't thought about what I'm doing in quite that way." I stopped speaking and stared at Lewis. He was still smiling, waiting for my response. "You know," I said, after a few seconds had passed. "You're probably right. That's exactly what I *have* done."

He laughed and said, "I thought it might be something like that."

I shook my head again, full of admiration for his perception. I almost felt like confessing to Lewis that I'd made up the business about *Cambridge Monthly* commissioning the article on Joan. But I suppressed the urge. I didn't want to spoil our rapport.

"Getting back to MacKenzie," Lewis said. "I gather the police don't consider him one of their primary suspects."

"No," I said. "In fact, I think he's pretty much out of the running."

Lewis nodded. "Somehow that doesn't surprise me. Even if there had been some physical evidence to connect him with what happened to Joan, I still wouldn't have picked him as the type who would have been likely to . . ."

"You've talked to the cops about this, then," I said.

"Oh, God, yes. There's been a detective in here every day this week. In fact, I was on the phone with one just before you came in."

"No wonder you didn't look pleased to see me when I told you I was here about Joan," I said.

"Oh, it's not that," Lewis replied. He scowled. "I'm happy to do whatever I can. Everybody here is. But the cops seem to have gotten it into their heads that whoever killed Joan was somebody connected with this place."

"Well," I said hesitantly, remembering the conversation I'd had earlier with Jack. "Isn't that a possibility?"

"I doubt it," Lewis said. "Look." He straightened up and leaned toward me slightly. His facial expression was very intense. "We deal with a lot of people here. It's true that some of them are severely disturbed. We have paranoiacs who are convinced that the C.I.A. is after them. We have schizophrenics who hear voices telling them to do things. *But*"—he put considerable emphasis on the word—"*but*, none of them is dangerous, to himself or to anybody else. If there were even a hint that one of the clients might be like that, we'd have spotted it and had him committed to a locked ward for observation." Lewis leaned back and took a deep breath. "There's no one like that under treatment at the center now."

"Wow," I said, taken slightly aback by the force in his voice.

Lewis relaxed and gave a brief, somewhat reluctant laugh. "Okay," he said. "I wasn't yelling at you. The thing is, I'm getting very tired of going over this."

"Sorry," I said.

Lewis leaned back in his chair and clasped his hands behind his head. "Forget it," he said. "It's a natural question. If I were the cops or you, *I'd* be asking it. It's just that . . ."

"Just that what?" I asked.

Lewis shook his head. "It's not easy to keep a place like this going. We don't have much money"—he gestured around him—"as you probably noticed from the elegance of the surroundings. And we don't have all the community support we'd like. There are people who want to see us shut down. So—" he shrugged. "All it takes is a rumor—no, not even that—a whisper that maybe one of our clients might possibly be involved in a murder and . . ." He looked at me. "You see the problem?"

"I think so," I said. "But if it's true that you have no clients that are potentially dangerous, then you have no cause for worry, do you?"

"Are you kidding?" Lewis said. "It doesn't matter that we don't have any dangerous clients. What matters is that somebody might think we do and try to use that as an excuse to get us shut down. I just explained that."

"Okay," I said placatingly. I could, in fact, see his point. "Yes, I guess you *do* have a problem."

"Yeah," Lewis said. He unclasped his hands and let them fall to the arms of the chair. Then he grinned at me, a wide, surprising burst of good humor. "Look, you didn't come here to listen to this. You wanted information about Joan. What else can I tell you?"

Somehow I didn't feel that this was the proper occasion to bring up Joan's personal life. "Just one thing," I said. "How was she as a counselor?"

"She was terrific," Lewis replied promptly. "Very bright, very enthusiastic. She had a real empathy for the people she worked with." He sighed. "What a waste."

I nodded. "I know." I flipped shut my notebook and dropped it back into my bag. Then I stood up. "I really should be going now," I said. "I've taken up an awful lot of your time."

Lewis lifted his right hand in a gesture of dismissal. "That's okay. Glad to help."

"Well, I appreciate it very much," I said smiling.

Lewis pushed himself up from his chair. "I'll walk with you to the door," he said.

The receptionist had left her post. The fat woman in the blue coat was still sitting in the waiting area. As far as I could tell, she hadn't moved a muscle the entire time I'd been in Lewis's office. She never glanced up as Lewis and I walked past her. I wondered what inner visions were holding her in thrall.

Lewis stopped with me at the door. I held out my hand and he took it.

"It was nice to meet you," I said. "And thanks again."

"Anytime," he said. "Come back if you have any more questions."

"Oh, I will," I assured him. "You've been awfully helpful."

He smiled and nodded and held the door open for me. "Well, I try."

10

RATHER THAN ANSWER any questions I'd had about Joan Stanley, my conversation with Peter Lewis had only served to raise a whole slew of new ones. I mulled over them during the walk back from Inman Square.

The possibility that Joan had been killed by one of the counseling center clients hadn't really occurred to me until Jack had pointed it out. Yet the more I thought about it, the more logical, perhaps even inevitable, the idea seemed. I recalled that my very first reaction to the murder was that it couldn't have been committed by anyone other than a consummate maniac. A homicidal necrophiliac, as I'd said to Jack. I found it beyond belief that any sane man—sane in either the medical or legal sense—could beat a woman to bloody death and then rape her repeatedly.

And Joan, working where she had, would have certainly come into contact with more than her share of loonies. I'd believed Lewis when he'd claimed that there were no dangerous clients undergoing treatment at the center. Or at least, I believed that Lewis himself might be convinced that this was true. But how could he be absolutely sure? The criminal law casebooks were bulging with stories about psychotic killers who'd managed to fool legions of psychiatrists into thinking that they were perfectly harmless. Hadn't there been a man in London in the fifties who'd not only gotten away with butchering a string of prostitutes (and caching bits of their corpses around his own house) but managed to convince the authorities that another man had committed the murders?

So I wasn't willing to accept Lewis's word on the subject as final, and neither, I suspected, was Jack. But I could still sympathize with Lewis's position. It was understandable of him to want to protect the center and its clients from what he might interpret as police harassment. Even healthy, stable people, innocent of any crime, react badly to being dragged into a murder investigation. What, then, might be the effect of such a thing on a group of people who weren't wrapped any too tightly to begin with?

That, however, was a side issue. Say that Joan had been killed by one of the counseling center clients. How, then, did such an assumption square with the fact that she'd apparently been murdered by someone with whom she'd been expecting to make love? No matter how you looked at it, there was no way around *that* contradiction.

The *manner* of Joan's death suggested very strongly that she'd been killed by a nut.

The *circumstances* of her death suggested very strongly that she'd been killed by a lover.

Would a woman accustomed to working with the mentally ill actually have let one of her male clients into her apartment while she was wearing nothing more than a silky, diaphanous nightgown—and then allow that person into the bedroom with her?

No way, unless she herself were nuts. And that, as far as I could tell, didn't seem to be the case.

Of course, if the downstairs apartment door had been open, the client could have sneaked in and surprised Joan. But if that had happened, why hadn't she tried to fight him off? Why hadn't she screamed? Why were there not even the slightest traces of a struggle in the apartment?

Then again, the guy might have come in brandishing a knife or a gun, and ensured her silence and cooperation that way. But even so, surely in the final moments, she'd have screamed or tried to put up some resistance. What, after all, would she have had to lose at that point?

But there wasn't the slightest indication that Joan had resisted her killer in any way.

There was, of course, the unappetizing possibility that Joan had had yet a third lover—a client of hers or of another counselor at the center. Someone seriously disturbed (that was the understatement of the year), but attractive and clever enough to conceal his real sickness from the probings of even a battery of trained therapists. God only knew how many people with *that* capability there were strolling the streets. A lot, from what I'd heard.

But then again—if Joan *had* been killed by one of her clients, where did that leave Kearns and Bingham? And why had Richie Kearns disappeared the day Joan had died? More interesting still, why hadn't he turned up since then? Surely he'd know that because he'd been Joan's fiancé, the police would have more than a passing interest in talking to him. If he were innocent, wouldn't he have come forward by now to be cleared of suspicion? It would be a simple process to compare his blood type and bite to those of the killer. If there weren't a match, he'd be off the hook.

And, if Kearns had loved Joan, wouldn't he at least have wanted to attend her funeral?

Christopher Bingham, it was true, hadn't skipped town after the murder.

50

But he wasn't helping his case by apparently trying to hide the fact that he'd been sexually involved with Joan. *That* alone certainly wasn't sufficient grounds for him to be taken into custody by the police, or even hauled off to a forensic orthodontist to have his bite mark taken and compared to an impression taken of the mark on Joan's breast. But still . . .

All right, then, maybe the murderer *had* been Kearns or Bingham. They both seemed to have motives. I knew that crimes of passion could be unspeakably gory and brutal, and that the people who committed them weren't necessarily crazy by any definition. But the manner of Joan's death had gone beyond plain gory brutality. Could either Kearns or Bingham be capable of committing the kind of insane necrophiliac violence that had been used on her?

By the time I got back to Central Square, I was in a worse state of confusion than I had been when I'd left Inman Square. I decided to bag the whole problem until I could talk it over with Jack.

I got a chance to do so later that evening, after he and I had taken care of some other urgent matters that had been on hold for the past week.

I described to him my meeting with Lewis, trying hard to keep all the details in sequence. I also recited to Jack the list of questions that were troubling me. He listened to the monologue very carefully, the way he always did when I told him my thoughts on some subject or other. It was one of his really endearing traits that he had such faith in my powers of observation and recall. And in my analytical skills.

"So," I said, rolling over on my stomach and propping myself up on my elbows. "I'm a little confused."

He smiled. "Join the club."

"Oh," I said. "Do you mean you've reached the same set of non-conclusions that I have?"

"Well, sort of."

"I'm flattered," I said. "To find I've been thinking along the same lines as the master detective."

"It was only a matter of time," he replied. I looked at him and we laughed.

I turned over and sat up. "Are you hungry?"

"Gawd, no. Are you?"

"Yes."

"Jesus. After the dinner you ate? How can you be?"

"It was all that healthful exercise," I said, throwing back the covers. "Excuse me." I got out of bed and went into the kitchen. In the refrigerator were some grapes. I washed them and put them in a bowl and took them back to the bedroom. I set the bowl on the night table and climbed back into bed. "Emergency rations," I explained.

I wiggled back down beneath the covers, pulling them up to my chin. It was another cold night. Jack slid an arm around me. I rested my head on his shoulder and said, "Explain something to me."

"Sure. What?"

"If whoever killed Joan wasn't Bingham or Kearns, how did he manage to do it without leaving his fingerprints on anything?"

"Either he didn't touch anything," Jack said. "Or he wore gloves."

I raised my head a little and stared at him. "Gloves?" I repeated.

"Sure."

"But . . ." I shook my head slowly. "What kind of gloves? Big woolly mittens?"

"Surgical gloves," Jack said. "It's been done. It's pretty common, in fact."

"Wait a minute," I said. "What are you telling me? That this guy walked into Joan's place, being very careful not to touch anything, went in the bedroom with Joan, got undressed, killed Joan, put on a pair of surgical gloves, raped her, then cleaned himself up and left?"

"Why not?"

"Yeah," I said, after a moment. "I suppose. God, how sickening." I fell back on the pillow. "You know, Jack, if it *was* some crazy that killed Joan—and I can't imagine that it wasn't—he was one hell of a careful planner."

"A lot of them are," Jack replied. "Crazy doesn't mean stupid. You haven't seen what I have."

"That's true," I said. I rolled over and lifted a small bunch of grapes from the bowl on the night table. "Want some of these?"

"Uh-uh."

"Okay." I pulled a few of the grapes from their stems and began popping them into my mouth. "You know," I said, "before I went to the counseling center this afternoon, I was almost positive it was Kearns or even Bingham who killed Joan. Now . . ." I shrugged.

"Why have you changed your mind?" Jack said.

I stopped eating and stared at him. "Because it was a nut who did it. You think so yourself. Is Kearns a crazy? Is Bingham?"

"Why not? Why couldn't either one of them be a closet psychopath? Just like your hypothetical client of Joan's?"

I blinked at him. "My God," I said. "I never even thought of that. God. Of course."

"Then on the other hand," Jack continued, "there's nothing definite yet that says it is Kearns or Bingham or even one of that crew at the counseling center. Maybe it's someone we don't know anything about."

"Or ever will," I added automatically.

He nodded. "There's that."

"Well," I said, trying to be encouraging, "at least you know the guy's blood type."

"Yeah. You know what percentage of the population has type A blood?"

"No."

"Forty."

"Oh." I was silent for a moment. "Well, you have one of his hairs."

"Proves nothing," Jack said. "Even if I had a sample to match it with, the best anybody could tell me was that there was a strong possibility that they were from the same source."

"Okay, even so," I countered. "What about the bite mark? That's unique, isn't it?"

"Sure. And it would be great if I had something to compare it to. I don't. So what do I do? Go around shoving plaster into the mouth of every guy in the greater Boston area till I find a match?"

I watched Jack as he spoke. He lay flat on his back, staring at the ceiling. His face was without expression and his tone of voice quite calm and neutral, neither self-pitying nor depressed. I understood. He was describing a situation that had happened too often for him to let it start haunting him.

"What time is it?" he asked.

I twisted around and looked at the clock on the night table. "Three-thirty."

"Three-thirty," he echoed. "Jesus. I have to get up at seven." He turned over on his side and closed his eyes. "'Night."

"'Night."

He was asleep in about five seconds. I smiled a little and settled back to finish the grapes.

I had met Jack a year and a half ago, when I'd gone to the police station to get some background material for an article I was writing on Famous Disappearances. After I'd gotten clearance from the chief, and convinced the then detective commander that I wasn't just another Cambridge crackpot or police groupie, I'd been passed on to Jack. But he hadn't really had the time to talk, and about the best I could say for his attitude toward me was that it was civil. Our conversation was brief and not very informative.

But I'm nothing if not persistent in my quest for the facts, and I went back to the police station the next day. Only I put off going there until late in the afternoon. My plan was that I'd get him to talk to me in his office for a while, and then I'd offer to buy him a drink so we could continue the conversation in a more relaxed environment. (Somebody told me that's the best way to get information out of cops.) At any rate, the plan worked, although not quite in the way I figured. I never got the chance to offer to buy him a drink; he offered to buy me one. Then he offered to buy me dinner. Sometime during the salad course it dawned on me that I thought he was interesting for a number of reasons other than simply what he knew about missing persons. I assume he thought the same about me, or else why spring for the meal? After that, things between us just sort of took off under their own steam, neither too quickly nor too slowly.

I'd never had any reason to be sorry they had.

Getting to know Jack had been an involved process. Some of it was that, like me, he didn't talk a great deal about himself. Part of it was that he didn't fit my image of a cop. (I'd since discovered that not many cops do.) He was, in the first place, very bright, and I suppose that in some awful, snobbish corner of my being I hadn't expected such a thing. I could still recall, with more than a momentary twinge of embarrassment, how surprised I'd been when he'd mentioned in an offhand way that he'd been in graduate school at the University of Chicago for two years. Although I suspected right off from the way he talked that he hadn't gone straight from high school to the police academy.

When I'd asked him why he'd left graduate school, he'd shrugged and replied that somewhere along the line, he'd realized that he didn't particularly want to teach. And there weren't an awful lot of career options for someone with a doctorate in history.

Following *that* revelation, it was inevitable that I ask him why he ended up becoming a cop. In answer to the question, he'd smiled and said that he couldn't think of anything else to do, and that even directing traffic and handing out citations for health ordinance violations beat selling insurance for a living.

I was sure there was more to it than that. He really seemed to enjoy the work, and I knew he was good at it. Maybe the leap from historical research to crime investigation had been a logical one for him to make. When you thought about it, writing a dissertation proving or disproving some theory and tracking down a murderer involved identical skills—like patience and the ability to piece together obscure and seemingly unrelated bits of evidence into some sort of coherent pattern.

And of course if you opted for the crime biz over the teaching biz, you'd be spared ever having to spend hours marking student papers, an exercise that could, in its own way, be as deadly as any gun-toting junkie.

Jack turned over and mumbled something I couldn't understand. Maybe it was "Turn out the light, huh?" I put the empty grape bowl on the night table, reached over and switched off the lamp, and slid down beside him.

11

MAYBE I'M PSYCHIC. The following morning, the editor I'd thought might be interested in a story on Joan Stanley's murder called me up and asked me if I'd be interested in writing a story on Joan Stanley's murder. I said yes. He said he expected something supersensational from me. I asked why. He said because I had a hot source of information in the police department. The inside track. Real meat. That's how Brandon Peters talks.

What Peters didn't know, of course, was that if I wrote for publication *everything* Jack had ever told me about crime in Cambridge, he wouldn't tell me anything.

Anyway, I was delighted to get the assignment. Now I had a legitimate reason—other than my own curiosity—to look into Joan's life. There's nothing like getting paid to snoop. Ask any detective.

What I had to do was get in touch with some of the people who'd known Joan really well and talk to them. Jack had mentioned to me the names of two of her friends, the two women who'd put him on to Christopher Bingham. If I could persuade either one or both of them to talk to me, and answer a few tactfully phrased questions, then I'd have some of the information I was seeking.

Too bad I couldn't remember their names.

I called Jack at his office. As usual, he wasn't in it, and I had to hang on for five minutes or so while somebody went to find him.

"Busy?" I inquired when he came to the phone.

"Moderately," he replied. "Unlike some people, I can't afford to spend the entire morning in bed."

"Drop dead," I said cheerfully. "You want to do me a favor?"

"Since you ask so nicely," he said, "how could I refuse?"

"Thank you. What are the names of those two girlfriends of Joan you told me about? The ones who blew the whistle on Bingham?"

"Why do you want to know?"

"For the story I'm doing. I gotta talk to *somebody* who'll tell me something about Joan."

"All right," he said. "They're Lisa Waite, and that's Waite, W-A-I-T-E, and Robin Peterson, like it sounds."

"Oh, good. Are they local?"

"Yeah. Waite lives on Ware Street and Peterson on, ah, let's see, Concord Avenue. I don't know the phone numbers off the top of my head. If you want, I'll check."

"That's okay," I said. "I'll find them. Thank you very much."

"No trouble. Listen, I really have to go now. I'll talk to you later, all right?"

"Certainly. Jack?"

"Yes?"

"I had a nice time last night."

"Me, too."

Smiling, I hung up the phone. Then I reached down to the lower shelf on the telephone table and pulled out the directory. I sat down cross-legged on the floor and flipped it open on my lap. There was a listing for an R. J. Peterson on Concord Avenue. I dialed the number and let it ring seven times. No answer. Damn. I looked up Lisa Waite's number and tried it. On the third ring someone picked up the phone and a breathless young female voice said, "Hello?"

"Hello," I said. "May I please speak to Lisa Waite?"

"This is Lisa."

It took some doing, but I was finally able to persuade her to talk to me about Joan Stanley. At first she was adamant about not saying anything at all. In fact, I thought she was going to slam down the receiver when I identified myself and told her what I wanted. Her reaction was a sort of exaggerated version of the one I'd gotten initially from Peter Lewis.

She softened up considerably when I told her that I'd been Joan's neighbor and that it had been I who'd discovered the body. I asked her if the press and the cops had been giving her a rough time. She said the cops hadn't been too bad (I'd have to remember to relay that news to Jack), but that there'd been two reporters camped on her doorstep when she'd returned home from Joan's funeral. And she'd been getting some peculiar phone calls from people she didn't know.

"Like me?" I inquired.

"You sound a lot more normal than the others," she replied.

"Well, in that case," I said quickly. "Would you like to meet me somewhere this afternoon and talk for a bit?"

There was silence for a few seconds on the other end of the line. Then she said, "Oh, all right. I guess so." She didn't sound thrilled at the prospect.

"Wonderful," I said, before she could change her mind. "Where and when?"

"Well, I have to do some errands in the square," she replied. "Would two o'clock be okay? In the Pamplona?"

"Perfect," I said. "I'll see you there."

"What do you look like?" she said.

"Tall," I said. "Red hair. I'll be wearing jeans and a fisherman's sweater and a tweed blazer."

"Okay," she said. "I'll find you."

The Pamplona is a subterranean coffeehouse on Bow Street in Harvard Square. The waiters wear white shirts and black ties. Three of the walls are whitewashed, and the fourth is covered by some kind of faded mural that I've never bothered to examine closely. There are pots of geraniums in the windows. The ceilings are very low, maybe just over six feet, and when I walk in there wearing high heels I have to keep my head bent so I won't crack it on a beam. If I sat in the Pamplona for too long, I always got to feeling like that Wilkie Collins character who wakes up in the middle of the night to find the canopy of the bed he's sleeping in descending on him.

Jack won't set foot in the place. He insists it reminds him of a holding tank in Marin County Police Headquarters.

I got to the Pamplona at five minutes to two. The place was filled with the usual sort of crowd that hangs out in Cambridge coffeehouses. Funky academe. A friend of mine claims to have seen Henry and Nancy Kissinger here once or twice. I never have. I suppose it's a question of being in the right place at the right time.

I spotted one unoccupied table for two in the far corner of the room and made for it, beating out a pair of midfortyish trendies in matching flak jackets. The waiter dropped a menu card in front of me as I was shrugging out of my blazer. I ordered an American coffee, spurning the espresso and mocha. Every time I drink something like that, my mouth tastes as if I've been chewing on pencils.

A few minutes after two, the door opened and a young woman in jeans and a Fair Isle sweater and down vest came in. She paused for a moment by the coat rack, peering around the room. I waved at her and smiled. She spotted me and threaded her way over to the table.

"Lise Waite?" I said.

She nodded.

"Sit down," I said. "Would you like some coffee?"

Lisa Waite yanked out the chair opposite me and flopped into it. We looked at each other appraisingly. She had a round, pale, smooth face and very long light brown hair held back by a tortoiseshell headband. She looked about sixteen. What were they letting into the graduate schools these days?

"Thank you for meeting me," I said. "I'm sure you had other"—I almost said *better*—"things to do this afternoon."

Lisa Waite shrugged. "It's all right."

"Well," I said. "I'll try not to keep you too long." I gestured at my cup. "How about some coffee?"

"I'll order something when the waiter comes by again. Thanks." Her manner wasn't precisely cool. More like guarded. I could understand why. But drawing her out on the subject of Joan might present some problems. I'd have to be careful how I phrased my questions.

"Before I say anything else," I began, "I want to tell you that I barely knew Joan. But I liked her very much."

Lisa Waite gave me a small polite smile.

"Tell me something about her," I suggested. "I really would like to get some feeling for the kind of person she was." I had a flash of recollection of Jack asking me a similar question last Sunday evening. It seemed like longer ago. And with all that had transpired since, did we know any more now than we had then? Or less?

Lisa pursed her lips consideringly. For a few moments she was silent. Then, "Joan was a really quiet person. It was sort of hard to get to know her."

"Well, *you* must have," I replied. "You and Robin Peterson were her closest friends, weren't you?"

"Oh, sure. I'm talking about other people. Joan didn't open up too quickly with strangers."

"So I guess you'd describe her as reserved, then," I said.

"Yeah, that's a good word. But she was friendly, you know? Nice to everybody. And it wasn't anything superficial, either. You had the feeling she was really concerned about people."

"That's interesting," I said. "Someone else just the other day told me almost the exact same thing about her. That she had a lot of—what? Empathy?"

"Oh, absolutely," Lisa said. She appeared to be warming to her subject. Maybe I *wouldn't* have to work to draw her out. "Joan was really great that way."

"Hardly surprising," I said. "In view of the kind of work she did. Although I gather warmth of personality isn't a prerequisite for becoming a therapist."

"Not really," Lisa said. "You should meet some of the people in the psych department . . ." She wrinkled her nose.

Without knowing it, she'd given me the perfect opening for the question I *really* wanted to ask. It would be a toughie, though.

"Lisa," I began. "I *may* call you Lisa?"

"Sure." She looked a little startled at the abrupt change of subject.

"Yes. Well." I paused and took a sip of my coffee. "What I'm going to say next will be a little awkward. I just want you to know that I have a very good reason for bringing the subject up."

Lisa sat back and gave me a speculative look. "It's about Joan and Bingham, isn't it?" she said. There was a distinct edge in her voice.

"Yes."

"I don't want to talk about it," she said.

I sighed. "Look," I said. "I know how you feel. But this is very important. I'm not on assignment from the *National Enquirer*. I'm not going to write some crap about how the professor and the coed shared a love nest."

Lisa just looked at me.

"This is very important," I repeated. "It's—I'm confused, that's all. This whole business with Bingham seems to contradict everything I've heard about Joan."

"Why do you think that?" Lisa asked quickly. She was assuming the psychology student's role, answering questions with questions.

I raised my eyebrows. "She didn't seem like the type to be fooling around with a married guy while she was supposed to be engaged to somebody else. That's what I want to clear up. I'm not interested in scandal. I've heard of lots worse than Joan and her professor, believe me."

Lisa didn't say anything.

"Please," I said. "If I don't understand this about Joan, then I'll never understand anything about her. You don't have to protect her reputation from me."

Lisa bit her lower lip. I kept my eyes on her face.

"Oh, God," she said finally. "All right."

I drew a long breath of relief. "Thank you."

She closed her eyes and nodded once, a very slight dip of the head.

"Before we get into it," I said, "would you like some coffee?"

"Okay."

I waved to the waiter and he came over to our table. "Another of these for me, please," I said, tapping my cup. I glanced at Lisa. "What would you like?"

"The espresso."

"And an espresso," I repeated to the waiter. He smiled and went away. I turned back to Lisa.

"Where do you want me to start?" she asked.

"Tell me how they got involved," I said. "Joan and Bingham."

"He was her adviser," Lisa said. "She was his teaching assistant. They were together a lot."

"And?"

"Well—" Lisa shrugged. "You know. It just sort of happened."

I shook my head. "But what about Richie Kearns?" I said. "Joan was involved with him when she got into this thing with Bingham, wasn't she? And she stayed with Kearns after that. Why? Why didn't she break it off with one of them?"

Lisa sighed. "Richie was part of the reason Joan started seeing Bingham."

"What?" I said, taken aback.

"It's kind of a long story."

I sat back and folded my hands on the table top. "Go ahead. I have all afternoon."

Lisa picked up her espresso. It looked the way it always does to me. Like sludge. "Joan and Richie were having problems."

"Oh. What kind of problems?"

Lisa curled her upper lip. "His, mostly. He was like, oh, I don't know, really possessive. It used to drive Joan crazy."

"What did he do?"

"Oh, stuff like hang around the psych department all the time. Be waiting for her after work."

"Well," I said cautiously, "that doesn't sound too obnoxious. I mean, if he loved her, he'd want to spend a lot of time with her, wouldn't he?"

"It wasn't like that," Lisa said. "It was like he was checking up on her all the time."

"Maybe he felt he had to," I argued, although without much conviction. "Joan must have told you she was being hassled by one of the clients at the counseling center. A guy named Andy MacKenzie. Maybe Kearns figured there might be trouble some time and he ought to be around to do something about it if there were."

Lisa shook her head. "That wasn't it. I knew when the thing with MacKenzie started. Richie was acting weird long before that."

61

"Okay," I said. "I'm with you so far. But what's all this got to do with Bingham?"

"Well," Lisa said, "I guess Joan just reached the point where she couldn't deal with Richie anymore and she just needed to be with someone else. Bingham was someone else."

"Maybe it was a kind of rebellion, too," I said, half to myself.

"What?"

"Well, if Kearns was all over Joan, implying to her all the time that he thought she was cheating on him, maybe she figured, hell, if he thinks I'm doing it, then I might as well go out and do it."

"That's true," Lisa said. "I never thought of it that way."

"It happens," I said. "A lot."

"Yeah," Lisa said. "I guess so."

I finished my coffee and set the cup back in the saucer. "Tell me," I said. "Do you think Joan was really in love with Bingham? Or do you think the whole thing was just a reaction to the way Kearns was treating her?"

"I don't know," Lisa said slowly. "I guess I thought she loved him. She said she did. I didn't think about it much."

"Was it true she was putting some pressure on Bingham to get a divorce?"

"Well, she told me she wanted to marry him. She said she talked to him about it."

"And he wasn't too happy with the notion, I gather."

"No."

"What's he like?"

"Who? Bingham?"

"Yes."

Lisa shrugged. "He's nothing special. In fact, he's kind of obnoxious. Conceited. He's one of those guys that thinks he's doing you a big favor if he says hello when he passes you in the hall."

"Sounds charming," I commented.

Lisa made a face. "Actually, I never could understand why Joan thought he was so terrific."

"Nobody ever understands things like that," I said, smiling.

"I guess not." She returned my smile, a little sadly.

"One more question," I said. "And then I'll let you go."

"Okay."

"I heard that Joan was going to tell Richie that as far as she was concerned, it was over between them. That the engagement or whatever was finished."

"Uh-huh. She told me she was going to tell him sometime last week."

62

"Okay. My question is this. Why the *hell* did she wait so long? Wouldn't things have been better all around if she'd broken up with Richie months ago? She'd have saved herself a lot of grief, wouldn't she?"

Lisa looked at me curiously. "Well, sure. But she didn't think she could do it. Break up with Richie, I mean."

It was my turn to look puzzled. "Why not?"

Lisa took a deep breath and let it out slowly. "She was afraid of him."

"*What?*"

"She was scared to death of Richie," Lisa reiterated firmly.

"Jesus," I said. "Why? I met him once. He didn't seem that ferocious to me. In fact, he seemed kind of sweet."

"You didn't know him," Lisa said. She gave a little contemptuous snort. "He had an awful temper. He was like crazy sometimes."

"Jee-zus," I repeated. "What are you telling me? That Kearns was unstable?" Why hadn't Jack mentioned this to me?

"Sort of," Lisa said. "I remember one night, God, it was months ago, Joanie was over at my apartment, and she stayed pretty late, and when she went home, Richie was there waiting for her. He started yelling at her and asking her where she'd been, and she got mad and told him it was none of his business, and he just went completely wild and started beating on her."

"God," I said, feeling a little chill. "And she never called the police or anything?"

"No. I asked her why she didn't and she told me she was even more scared of what he might do to her afterward if she did."

"This is awful," I murmured. I felt a little stunned. I'd known someone once, years ago, who'd done to me almost exactly what Kearns had done to Joan. Lisa's story was bringing back things I thought I'd left behind me long since.

"That's not all there is to it," Lisa said.

"What do you mean?"

"Well"—she paused and took a deep breath—"Richie told Joanie that if she ever left him, or if anything ever happened to break them up, that he might . . ."

"Might what?" I prompted, with the feeling I already knew.

Lisa looked uncomfortable. "Well, I guess—what Joan told me was that he said he'd kill himself."

"Oh, Christ," I said.

"Huh?" She looked a little surprised at my reaction.

"Nothing. It's a line I've heard before, that's all. Okay, go on, Lisa. Richie threatened to kill himself. Did he threaten Joan?"

"I don't know."

"Lisa," I said. "This is important. Do you think it's possible that Richie could have killed Joan?"

Lisa looked even more ill at ease than she had before. "I don't know," she repeated.

"But the thought's occurred to you, hasn't it?"

She hesitated a moment and then nodded.

I slumped a little in my chair. "What did the police say when you and Robin Peterson told them about Richie being a flippo?"

"I don't understand."

"The police. What did they say when you told them about Kearns?"

She was silent, looking at the table top. I had a sudden nasty suspicion. "Lisa," I said softly. "You *did* mention this to the cops, didn't you?"

"No," she replied, almost inaudibly.

"Jesus Christ," I said. The couple at the next table glanced at me curiously. I closed my eyes and counted slowly to ten. When the impulse to reach across the table and grab Lisa Waite by the collar and shake her till her teeth rattled had subsided, I opened my eyes. "Why the hell didn't you say anything about Richie before now?" I hissed.

She looked vaguely offended. "I figured the cops already knew about him."

"God," I said. "Now how would they unless you and Robin told them?"

"Well," Lisa said, somewhat petulantly. "I figured Bingham told them. He knew, didn't he? Joan was always crying on his shoulder about what a creep Richie was. He could have said something."

"I don't believe this," I said. "Lisa, Bingham didn't tell the cops a goddamned thing. He even denied having an affair with Joan."

Lisa's eyes widened. "Oh, my God. Are you serious?"

"Do I sound as if I'm kidding?" I demanded. I reached into my handbag and took three dollars from my wallet and put them on the table to cover the check and tip. Then I rose, plucking my blazer off the back of my chair.

"Are you leaving?" Lisa said.

"Yes, and not by myself, either," I replied.

She looked bewildered.

"Babe," I said. "If you have any big plans for this afternoon, I suggest you consider them cancelled as of this moment."

"What? What for?"

"You and I are taking a walk to Central Square," I said, "where you are going to sit yourself down in the police station and repeat to the cops everything, and I mean *everything*, about Richie Kearns you've just told me."

64

"Wait a minute," Lisa said. "I have to go to the library later. I mean I have a paper due Monday. Can't it wait till then?"

I stared at her in disbelief. "Lisa, honey," I said, "you have a choice. You can either walk to the police station alongside me like a grown-up person or I drag you by the hand. Or maybe by the hair. Which will it be?"

"I'm coming," she said.

12

As it turned out, I was a lot more disturbed about what Lisa Waite had done, or rather failed to do, than Jack was.

"Happens all the time," he said. It was six o'clock, and we were sitting in his office hashing over the events of the afternoon. A considerably chastened Lisa Waite had left a half-hour earlier. I hadn't had to make good on my threat to haul her by the hair down to the police station. In fact, she'd been remarkably cooperative. Probably I'd scared the shit out of her.

"I don't know, Jack," I said. "The fact that stuff like that does happen all the time would bother me. But you didn't even seem surprised that Lisa'd been holding out on you."

"I wasn't," he said. "When I first talked to her, I knew she knew something she wasn't telling me. I figured it had to do with either Kearns or Bingham."

"How'd you know that?" I asked, surprised.

He smiled. "I've been doing this a long time. You do get a feel after a while for who's lying, or who's keeping something back."

"Did you believe her?" I asked. "I mean, about what she said about how she and Robin Peterson didn't say anything to you about Kearns because they thought you'd already heard about him from Bingham?"

"Oh, sure I believed her. That's usually why people don't tell cops things. Or one of the reasons, anyway. They tell us what they think we should know."

"Well, there's that." I grinned at him. "You could look at it this way, though. Maybe Lisa and Robin were afraid you wouldn't be able to handle any really sordid details about what went on between Joan and Richie."

"Yeah, maybe."

"Be that as it may," I said, "will what Lisa told you be any help?"

"Well, it confirms, or at least it adds weight, to something I'd already guessed."

"Which is?"

Jack leaned back in his chair and put his feet on the desk blotter. "That Kearns is not wrapped too tightly."

"I'll say," I said. "He sounds to me like a total loonie. But . . . how did you figure that?"

Jack clasped his hands behind his head. "I got his service records this morning. He got a medical discharge from the army in 1971."

"Ooohhh," I said. "Let me guess. On psychiatric grounds, right?"

"Yup."

"So?"

"So I did a little poking around. Turns out he's been in and out of therapy for the past—what? Thirteen, fourteen years now."

"God," I said. "You didn't find that out from his shrink, did you? Don't they refuse on principle to discuss their patients with cops?"

"Some do, some don't. But no, I didn't find this out from Kearns's shrink. I got it from one of his friends. With a little persuasion."

"Ah-hah," I said. "So what's Kearns's problem? Other than the fact that he beats up his girlfriends and maybe even kills them."

Jack yawned. I had to remind myself that he'd had very little sleep the previous night. "The friend says Richie's been suffering from, and I quote, posttraumatic stress disorder."

"Of course," I said. "The Vietnam vet's disease."

"Uh-huh."

"So what does that entail?"

"You want the list of symptoms I got from David?" David was David Epstein, a psychiatrist Jack and I knew socially. Sometimes we consulted him for separate professional reasons.

"Sure."

"Okay." Jack leaned forward and took a piece of paper from the desk. He held it up and recited, "Depression. Startle reactions. Traumatic war dreams. Flashback phenomena. Dissociative episodes. Possible Schneiderian first-rank symptoms of schizophrenia including disorientation and memory impairment."

"Never mind the bullshit," I said. "How does any of that relate to Kearns?"

"According to the friend, Richie had every symptom on the list. In spades."

"Jesus," I said softly. "But . . . how did he function? Kearns was in graduate school. I mean, granted it was only the education department he was in, but even so, he must have gotten some of his act together to go to classes and do a thesis and all. And he never did anything weird enough to get him arrested or committed. At least, not that anybody knew about."

"Oh, yeah." Jack leaned back again in his chair. "Well, the friend told me he thought Richie was over the worst of it. That he'd really improved in the past year or so."

"Oh, God," I said, laughing half in disgust and half in amusement. "Everybody involved in this case is some kind of amateur shrink, right? They've all got these incredible insights into the human psyche. And nobody knows what the hell is going on. What do you hear from Kearns's family?"

"What family? He doesn't have one. He was an only child. Parents died in a car crash in Pittsburgh seven years ago."

"Oh," I said. "Well, I guess he didn't run home to them in his time of trouble, did he?"

"Nope."

"And you still have no idea of where he might be? The friend was no help on that point?"

"Uh-uh."

"Whooo," I said, shaking my head. "Jack, dear?"

"Yes?"

"You got some problems."

"Yeah. Tell me about them."

"No. I won't do that. I'll ask you another question."

"What's that?"

"How about Joan's family? Could they give you anything useful? After all, Kearns was engaged to their daughter. They must have met him at least once or twice."

Jack shook his head, smiling. "Oh, yeah, they'd met him. But as far as they knew, Kearns was just some guy Joan dated. She never said anything to them about any engagement. And they didn't know anything about any problems she might be having with him."

"Wow," I said. "Between what you're saying and what Lisa said, I'm getting the very strong feeling that this alleged intense relationship Joan and Richie were having was all in his mind."

"Maybe," Jack said. "But with all due respect to Joan, you gotta admit she did a lot to feed the delusion. I mean by not breaking up with Kearns earlier on, when she first realized he wasn't too stable."

"But that's exactly why she couldn't, Jack," I said. "God! Weren't you listening to what Lisa was saying? Kearns threatened to kill himself if Joan left him. Probably she figured he was just wacked out enough to do it.

And if he did, where did that leave her? Carrying around a load of guilt for the rest of her life? My boyfriend took the pipe because I was mean to him?"

Jack looked a little dubious, or at least I thought he did.

"You don't understand," I said. "I don't think you could unless something like that had happened to you." As soon as the words were out of my mouth, I bit the inside of my lower lip. I hadn't meant to say them.

Jack continued to look at me. His facial expression had shifted a little, from dubious to something else I couldn't quite interpret.

"Okay," he said. "Tell me. I want to understand this."

"Never mind," I muttered.

"Nope," he said. "You brought it up. You have to follow through on it. You can't get away with telling me I can't understand something and then refuse to explain why."

I sighed. "You don't give up easily, do you?"

"Uh-uh. Tell me."

I crossed my legs and hunched over a little in my chair. Self-revelation, even with Jack, always makes me a little bit nervous. "This happened a long time ago. When I was in my last year of graduate school. Jesus." I glanced up at Jack. "Maybe there's something in the academic environment that fosters this kind of lunacy."

"Maybe. Go on."

"All right, all right. I started going out with this guy. From my standpoint, it was no big romance, but he apparently got the idea, please don't ask me how, that he and I were in love and should get married."

"So?"

"So the weird thing was, he just sort of assumed I felt the same way. He never even *asked* me if I wanted to marry him. He just figured I did, and he started making all these plans for our future. Like how we were going to have five kids right away, and I was going to not work and stay home and be a good wife and mother and scrub toilets all day."

Jack smiled a little. "Did you enlighten him otherwise?"

"Well, that's the whole point. I *couldn't*. Every time I tried to suggest to him, no matter how gently, that maybe I ought to be consulted about what it was I wanted to do with the rest of my life, he'd just—just flip out. Pretty soon it got to a point where we were just fighting all the time."

"So why didn't you end it?"

"For the same reason Joan didn't call it off with Richie. I couldn't. The more I tried to detach myself from this guy, the more clingy-clutchy he got. It was horrible, Jack. After a while, I couldn't get away from him. I'd come home from school and he'd be there, waiting for me. He wanted to know exactly what I was doing all the time when I wasn't with him. It was like—I don't know, some kind of maniacal desperation."

"Trying to hold onto something he never had to begin with," Jack said.

"Yeah. That was it, I guess. And, my God, he was so *jealous*. I remember once my sister had to drive up to Vermont on business and stay overnight in Bennington, and she asked me if I wanted to come along. So I said sure. But when I told this fool, his name was Gordon, if that matters, that I was going to be away for a day, he reacted like I'd just announced I was running off to Paris with another man for three weeks. It was grotesque. You're not going to believe this, but he even said, 'How can you do this to me?'"

"Oh, shit," Jack said. "So what happened after that?"

"Well, it just degenerated into the most hysterical mess. I had my first teaching job at that point—he didn't have a job, and I wonder how much *that* had to do with things—"

"A lot," Jack interrupted. "Believe it. Excuse me. Go on."

"Okay. Well, he wanted me to quit work and live with him, and when I said no, he screamed at me that I wasn't a real woman and that I was sick and warped."

"Sick and warped because you didn't happen to love him," Jack remarked.

"There was that," I said. "But I was also sick and warped because I wasn't the kind of person he thought I was. Or so he said. And you know damn well when somebody says that to you, they don't mean you're *better* than they thought."

"That's rarely the case," Jack agreed. He gave me a slight, sympathetic smile. "So you were the merchandise that didn't live up to its billing, right?"

"I guess not. But you know, one of the other strange things about the whole business was that he always insisted that one of the reasons he loved me was that I was smart and independent and able to take care of myself. But he got absolutely outraged whenever I acted that way. So what the hell did he want from me?"

"Damned if I know," Jack said. "He ever threaten you? Hurt you?"

"Nooo, not directly," I said slowly. "But he sort of implied that he might do away with himself if I ever left him. That, of course, was before he decided what a sicko neurotic I was for not wanting to marry him."

"So how did it end up?" Jack asked. He raised an eyebrow at me. "I'm assuming it did end up? He's not still following you around accusing you of being unwomanly?"

"Oh, it ended, all right," I said, making a flipping gesture with my right hand. "He just took off one day. Vanished. I never heard from him again, thank God. And after all that fighting and hysteria and oh how I love you I worship you and I'll jump off a pier if you ever leave me and don't you adore me as much as I adore you you better if you know what's good for you. Please don't ask me what became of him, because I haven't the vaguest notion." I sagged back in the chair and closed my eyes. Curiously, I felt terribly drained, as if I'd just run a marathon.

"That's quite a story," Jack said, after a moment.

I opened my eyes and blinked at him. "Yeah, well, you haven't heard the last of it."

"I haven't?"

"Nope. Did I mention that Gordon had been married once already?"

"No."

"Well, he had. And he confided to me that the only reason he *did* get married was that the woman he was with threatened to kill herself if he didn't."

"Oh, Christ," Jack said, and burst out laughing. He slapped a hand over his mouth and said, "Jesus, I'm sorry. I didn't mean to do that."

"Don't be," I said. "Laugh all you want. The whole thing *is* kind of hilarious, in a sick way. Anyhow, it's been on my mind ever since Lisa started telling me about Joan's problems with Richie."

"Yeah, I can imagine," Jack said.

I smiled at him. "Are you sorry you asked me about it?"

He scowled. "Don't be idiotic. I'm glad you told me." He paused and added, "It explains some things about you."

I gave him a wide-eyed ingenue stare. "Oh, Jack. You're *not* going to tell me you've just realized I'm not the woman you thought I was, are you?"

"Not at all. I love you just the way you are."

"Oh, puke," I said. We looked at each other and started to laugh.

"Nice talk," Jack said. He glanced at his watch. "Especially since I was just going to ask you if you wanted to go somewhere and get something to eat."

Self-revelation not only makes me nervous, it makes me hungry. "An inspired suggestion," I said.

"Okay, then." Jack got up and started putting on his jacket.

We walked, without saying anything more, from the station and down Western Avenue toward Central Square. The temperature had dropped about ten degrees since sunset, and a sharp wind cut down through the buildings on either side of us. I shivered a little in the thin blazer. Jack sensed it and put his arm around me.

"You going to wait till February to break out your winter coat?" he asked.

"I was thinking maybe March," I said.

He laughed and squeezed my shoulders. "This is Massachusetts, honey, not South Carolina."

"Jack," I said. "When you were talking to David Epstein, did he say whether he thought it was possible for someone with Kearns's kind of problems to have done what—what happened to Joan?"

"Well, you know David. He doesn't like to speculate."

"But still," I persisted. "Nobody's asking him to finger Kearns. All I'm asking is if there's even a remote chance that Richie might be crazy enough to kill."

Jack didn't answer me for a moment.

"Well?" I said.

Jack sighed. "Yeah. He said it was possible."

"God," I said softly. I looked over at Jack. "What do *you* think?"

"I don't know."

We came to the intersection of Massachusetts and Western avenues.

"His blood type is A," Jack said abruptly.

"What?"

"Kearns," Jack said. "He has the same blood type as the killer."

13

SUNDAY I SPENT trying to make some sense of all that I'd learned over the preceding forty-eight hours.

I was beginning to understand a good deal of what had previously puzzled me about Joan Stanley.

I was also beginning to regret that I'd never had the chance to get to know her better. It seemed we'd had some things in common.

What really bothered me was the extent to which I'd misread Richie Kearns's character. *You didn't know him*, Lisa Waite had said. True enough. But even on the basis of only one brief meeting, I'd have been willing to make book that Kearns was the antithesis of the violent type.

My mental image of him was that of a stocky guy maybe five-eight or five-nine, with crinkly dark brown hair and a bushy reddish brown beard and mustache. He had very fair skin, I recalled, the kind that reddens after ten minutes' exposure to the sun or wind. Not handsome, and too short for me to find attractive, but kind of appealing in a teddy-bearlike way.

His manner had matched his appearance. When Joan had introduced me to him, he'd smiled almost shyly and taken my hand in a gentle, slightly damp clasp. When he'd asked me about my work, he'd sounded genuinely interested in the reply. In answer to *my* question, he'd told me he was studying early childhood education. I'd had an instantaneous vision of him cavorting on a playground with a gang of four- and five-year-olds. Somehow the image wasn't absurd. There was something of the overgrown, hirsute child about Kearns himself.

All in all, he had projected the sort of quiet friendliness that to my mind had characterized Joan. I'd assumed that shared quality had been one of the things that had drawn them together. Maybe it had been, initially.

Kearns had sure fooled *me*.

I was pondering this when there was a rap at my apartment door. Lucy, sprawled semicomatose on the rug before the fireplace, raised her head. Alert.

"Who is it?" I yelled, a little annoyed at having my meditations disturbed.

There was an indistinct murmur from the other side of the door. I got up from the couch and crossed the room. Lucy rose reflexively and trailed after me. "Who?" I repeated.

"Peter Lewis," the voice replied, much more loudly. There was a little pause. "From the counseling center in Inman Square. You came to see me the other day."

"Oh," I said, startled. "Just a minute." Automatically, I glanced in the mirror over the fireplace. My sweater was clean and my hair didn't appear to be any more disheveled than it usually was. I went to the door and opened it. Lewis was standing on the threshold, a cardboard box in his arms. He gave me an apologetic smile.

"Sorry to barge in on you like this," he said.

"That's okay," I replied, still surprised but not precisely displeased to see him. I opened the door wider. "Come in."

"Thanks." He stepped over the doorsill and into the living room. Lucy, that big bold guardian of hearth and home, wandered back to her place on the rug and collapsed.

"Don't mind the dog," I said. "She's a little standoffish at first with people she doesn't know. Give her a moment to sniff around and she'll be slobbering all over you. Her name's Lucy, by the way."

"Hello, Lucy," Lewis said. From her vantage point on the rug, the dog gave Lewis the once-over. Then she raised her left hind paw and began clawing vigorously at her left ear.

"Before I ask you to sit down," I said, "may I ask you a rather inhospitable question?"

Lewis looked taken aback and then amused. "Sure."

"How did you get in here? I mean, inside the building?"

"Oh." Lewis tilted his head in the direction of my apartment entrance. "Your downstairs door was open."

"*Dammit*," I said. "That *idiot*."

"I beg your pardon?"

I shook my head. "Sorry. I didn't mean you. It's just that the jerk who lives upstairs must go in and out of this building at least twenty times a day, and half the time he doesn't bother to shut the front door behind him."

Lewis's facial expression faded from amused to concerned. "That's not very safe for you and the other tenants, is it?"

"You're telling me?" I replied. "The door was open last Sunday night when . . ." I shook my head vigorously, as if to chase away the memory. "The thing is, *any* kind of creep could wander in here, *any* time."

"Thanks," Lewis said, in tones of great gravity.

I realized that I had been something less than tactful. "I didn't mean you," I said.

"Good." Lewis grinned at me and then glanced up at the ceiling. "Seriously, though, that *is* a problem, isn't it? Have you talked to the guy?"

I rolled my eyes. "You don't know this jerk," I said. "It's pointless to try and communicate *anything* to him. He does more drugs than the entire audience at a Grateful Dead concert. I don't think he knows his own name, half the time. I heard the landlord was going to get after him about the door business, but—" I shrugged. "If he did, it obviously didn't make much impression."

"That's too bad," Lewis said. He shifted the cardboard box a little in his arms. It looked heavy. I realized I'd never gotten around to asking him to sit down.

"Why don't you set that thing down?" I said, gesturing at the box. "And yourself."

"Oh. Okay, thanks. This *is* sort of heavy." He glanced around him, as if trying to determine the best possible place to deposit his burden. I watched him covertly as he did so. I hadn't fully noticed it before, but he was a good-looking guy, with curly black hair and heavy-lidded hazel eyes set in a thin dark face. Sexy. His female clients probably dreamt about him.

He still wasn't a patch on Jack.

"So," I said, resuming my seat on the couch. "What can I do for you?" As I spoke the words, it dawned on me how ambiguous they sounded and I winced internally.

If Lewis picked up on the unintentional double entendre, he gave no sign of it. He remained standing by the coffee table, gazing down at me. "Well, I was going to ask you a favor."

I raised my eyebrows. "Oh?"

He nodded. "The thing is, we were clearing out Joan's office at the center yesterday, and we found a lot of stuff that we really didn't think we should just throw out. I mean, not without asking someone about it first."

"I see," I said. "I take it that's what's in the box."

"Yes."

I smiled. "Well, I'd love to help you, but I'm afraid you're asking the wrong person. I must have told you that I barely knew Joan. I wouldn't feel right making any decision about how her property should be disposed of."

"Oh, no." Lewis looked horrified at the very notion. "I wasn't going to ask you to do that. It was just that I was wondering if you wouldn't mind keeping the stuff"—he nodded at the box—"until her family or whoever

75

comes to pick up the things from her apartment." He gave me a questioning look. "They haven't done that yet, have they?"

"No," I replied. "Not as far as I know."

Lewis looked relieved. "Well, then, maybe if it's not too much trouble for you . . ."

"Not at all," I said. "Next time I see the landlord, I'll just ask him to let me into Joan's place and I'll leave the box on the living room couch or something. Will that be okay?"

"Hey, that's terrific," Lewis said. "I'd really appreciate it."

"No trouble," I said.

"That's great," he said. "Look, I wrote a note explaining what the stuff is and where it came from." He reached into his coat pocket and took out a small white envelope and handed it to me.

"Fine," I said. "I'll just tape it to the top of the box." I set the envelope on the arm of the sofa.

"Ah, that's great," Lewis repeated. "Thanks a lot."

"Hey," I said. "It's no problem at all." I glanced at the box. "What's in there, anyway?"

"Oh, nothing particularly valuable," Lewis said. "Mostly books. A cup. Some pictures. You know. Just the usual stuff people have in offices."

"Okay," I said. "Just so long as I'm not being given custody of an emerald necklace or anything."

"Nope." Lewis smiled. "Nothing like that."

"Good." I returned his smile.

There was a little silence. Lewis and I continued to smile at each other. Should I ask him to stay and have a cup of coffee? That way, I'd be able to pump him a bit more about Joan. On the other hand, he struck me as a pretty circumspect, as well as perceptive, guy and he might see through the ploy and be irritated by it. That would be embarrassing. Shit.

Lewis solved the dilemma for me. "I really have to be going," he said. "I only dropped by for a minute. I have an appointment in Boston at three."

Relieved, yet nonetheless obscurely disappointed, I rose from the couch. "Then I certainly won't keep you," I said. I looked at my watch. "You know, it's two-forty-five now."

"God," Lewis said in horror. "I have to move. It'll take me at least fifteen minutes to find a place to park." He gave me another smile. "Thanks again. I mean, for keeping Joan's stuff."

"Like I said," I replied. "It's no trouble." I walked with Lewis to the apartment door.

"Don't bother to come downstairs with me," he said. "I can let myself out."

"Sure." I opened the apartment door. "Well, it was nice to see you again."

"You, too," he said. He paused for a second and then added, in hushed, conspiratorial tones, "Don't worry."

I blinked in surprise. "Don't worry?" I repeated. "Worry about what?"

He grinned. "The downstairs door. I promise to shut it behind me."

14

WHILE IT'S TRUE that I make most of my living doing free-lance writing, I occasionally have to take on other jobs just to keep Lucy in Alpo, me in vodka, and a roof over both our heads. Sometimes I'll teach a freshman composition course at one of the local colleges. (Harvard and Tufts pay the best, so I try to hit them up before I sign on anyplace else.) Sometimes I'll do free-lance editing for magazines with titles like *Fossil Fuels Quarterly* or *Microchip Age*. And sometimes I'll do private tutoring, mostly of high school students whose S.A.T. scores aren't high enough to get them into Wellesley or Williams or even B.U. The work pays well, but I never come away from a tutorial without a fresh appreciation of the joys of *not* having to teach full-time for a living.

Monday afternoon I had a particularly trying session. My client was a senior at Rindge and Latin who'd scored an impressive 324 on his verbal S.A.T. Since you get 200 points just for putting your name on the test form, I didn't hold out much hope that I was going to turn this character into a hot contender for a Rhodes scholarship. He could barely read the operating instructions on a video cassette. The kid didn't care; he wanted to be the next Elvis Costello. But Mom and Dad were thinking more in terms of premed or prelaw, and they were willing to reimburse me (well) for helping to nurture their delusions.

I wasn't being paid to have fun, either. When the tutorial ended, I had the kind of headache I hadn't had since the last time I'd attended an English department curriculum committee meeting. I decided to treat myself to a drink at the nearest bar.

The nearest bar was Christopher's on Mass. Avenue in Porter Square. Christopher's isn't really a bar in either the low-down-whuddya-got-on-draft-let's-drink-to-get-drunk sense of the term or the spritzer-Brandy-Alexander-White-Russian-Singapore-Sling-Harvey-Wallbanger-do-you-come-here-often-I'm-a-sensitive-caring-nonsmoking-thirty-seven-year-old-divorced-management-consultant-into-running-and-tennis-and-cooking-and-therapy-let's-have-a-meaningful-fuck sense of the term. It's just a place you can have a drink and a cheeseburger or chili or nachos and play Ms. Pac-Man or watch the six o'clock news or count the checks in the blue and white tablecloths. On Friday and Saturday nights they have live bluegrass or folk or jazz in the side room. I go there every once in a while on a week night when I feel like being alone but not isolated from humanity. I can even write in the place undisturbed.

When I walked into Christopher's, there were maybe three people at the bar and another six at the tables scattered around the room. That's another thing I like about the place. Even at its busiest, it's never like high noon at the George Washington's Birthday Sale in Filene's basement.

I got myself a small round table for two and settled into it. The waitress materialized after a few minutes and took my order for a vodka martini on the rocks, no olive, no twist. I love olives, and I certainly don't have anything against lemons, but ever since I read somewhere that a lot of bars recycle, so to speak, their garnishes, I've been taking my drinks minus anything but ice. I have absolutely no use for an olive that's already made the swish circuit in someone else's martini.

The waitress brought me my drink, along with a bowl of tortilla chips and some mild sauce. I was restrained; I didn't snatch the glass from her hand and drain it in one continuous motion. I waited for her to set the drink on the table. After the first swallow I could feel the pressure on my temples begin to ease. Nature's own tranquilizer.

I really don't drink all that much. But when I do, I *enjoy* it.

The six o'clock news was coming on. I took a second sip of my drink and settled back to watch. The bartender left off polishing beer glasses and reached up and fiddled with the color control on the television over the bar. I put my chin on my fists and fixed my gaze on the T.V. screen. There was a pitch for Subaru and then an anchorman came on and said something about a crisis in the Israeli Parliament and an uproar at a Boston City Council meeting. The co-anchor followed up with a story about a minor (?) accident at the Maine Yankee Atomic Power Plant and some further details about a general alarm fire in a Newton housing complex for the elderly. Business as usual. After about three minutes, I went back to my food and drink. I'm not uninterested in what goes on in the world or in the Commonwealth of Massachusetts, and I hope I'm not callous, but I could have sworn I'd already heard the same stories three times in the past week.

I was halfway through the tortilla chips and three quarters of the way through the martini when I heard the anchorman say, "This word just in to the Channel Five newsroom. An apparent hostage situation has developed in a house on Remington Street in Cambridge." I looked up sharply. "We go now to Sheila McAndrew for a live report," the anchorman continued.

The screen went blank for a few seconds. I sat upright, staring at it, feeling a little jangle of apprehension in my stomach. "Hostage situation."

Jack was a hostage negotiator. He'd been involved in a number of "hostage situations." He'd also been shot at a couple of times in "hostage situations," once by a Puerto Rican nationalist and once by a laid-off construction worker whose wife had walked out on him, taking the kids, the car, and the bank account.

I half rose from my seat and called to the bartender, "Turn it up." He paused in the middle of filling a plastic pitcher with draft Miller and threw me a surprised look. "The television," I said, less peremptorily. "Please?" The bartender shrugged, reached up, and raised the volume on the television. One of the topers at the bar swung around on his stool to stare at me. I ignored him.

The gray blankness on the screen dissolved and coalesced into a shot of a narrow, curving, tree-lined street. I sank back into my chair, not taking my eyes off the television. The camera zeroed in on a young, pretty, dark-haired woman in a fur-collared beige coat. She was standing on the corner of Remington and Harvard streets. Behind her I could see that Remington was jammed solid with police cars, blue lights revolving. There were dozens of cops, in and out of uniform, moving back and forth and looking fearsomely purposeful. I didn't see Jack, but that didn't mean he wasn't there.

In response to some off-screen cue, the reporter raised a hand mike to her lips and began speaking. "Ted," she said, as if talking face to face to the anchorman in the studio, "details are sketchy, but the situation as it stands is apparently that there is a man armed with a shotgun on the second floor of the building about a hundred feet behind me." The camera moved slightly to focus on a three-story mustard-colored frame house with a sort of King Arthur turret running up one side. Then the camera swiveled back to the reporter. "We don't know for sure at this point if the man is holding any hostages," Sheila McAndrew continued. "We *do* know, however, that he *has* threatened to shoot anyone attempting to approach the building. The police have so far failed to establish contact with the man. As you can see, Remington Street has been cordoned off, and no one is being allowed to enter the area. With me here is Lieutenant Anthony De Christo of the Cambridge Police Department." Next to the reporter stood a middle-sized, chunky man in uniform. He looked as if he needed a shave. He also looked as if he wished he were someplace else, preferably in the familiar confines of a patrol supervisor's car.

"Lieutenant De Christo," Sheila McAndrew said. "What steps have you and your men taken to defuse this situation?"

De Christo cleared his throat and said, "We've evacuated all civilian personnel from the immediate vicinity. We have an ambulance standing by." He sounded as if he were reciting from the C.P.D. Operations Manual. He probably was. "Vehicular and pedestrian traffic is being directed away from the area. The containment team unit has been deployed." Containment team unit, I knew, was a police euphemism for the guys with the firepower and the flak jackets. The shooters.

"Yes," Sheila McAndrew replied, as if everything De Christo was saying made perfect sense to her. "Can you tell us, Lieutenant, if there's any definite indication yet whether the gunman may be holding any hostages?"

"Not that we've been able to determine," De Christo said stolidly.

"I see. Has the gunman made any demands?"

"Not as of this point in time."

Sheila looked faintly disappointed. "What about his identity? Has that been established?"

At that moment a man in a windbreaker and Levis, a plainclothes cop, I assumed, came up to De Christo and said something to him, in tones too low for the reporter's mike to pick up. He and De Christo wheeled around and walked off to join three other cops standing by one of the police cruisers.

Sheila McAndrew turned back to face her cameraman. She lifted the mike to her face and said, "As you can see, Ted, there seems to be considerable uncertainty here as to how this situation developed and what the gunman's purpose is. Apparently—"

There was a loud popping noise. I flinched and drew a deep, ragged breath; I knew what that sound was. The image on the television screen bounced wildly up and down. Sheila McAndrew vanished. The camera steadied and refocused. It caught a close-up of a cop in plainclothes streaking across Remington in a low, crouching run. He was carrying a rifle.

Sheila McAndrew reappeared on screen. Her face was pale and frightened, but she was plainly going to hang in there. She brought the hand mike up and said, "The gunman has just fired a shot into the street." Her voice was remarkably level and controlled. "He was apparently aiming at a group of police officers positioned behind the police cruiser directly across the street. No one has been hit." She paused and repeated firmly, "*No one has been hit*. So far, the police have not returned any fire."

The television screen went blank momentarily, and then the image of the anchorman reappeared. He was staring off to his left, as if transfixed. The director or someone must have signaled him, for he swung back to face the camera and said, "Thank you, Sheila. Our live coverage of the drama unfolding on Remington Street has been temporarily disrupted. We'll be bringing you further details of that story as they come in, and of course Channel Five will be staying on the scene until the situation with the gunman has been resolved. Former West German chancellor Helmut Schmidt today . . ."

I slumped in my chair and took another deep breath. Little cold thrills of apprehension were chasing up my neck and across my shoulders. *Where was Jack in all this?* He was a trained hostage negotiator, as well as second-in-command of the detectives, and in either capacity he'd probably be one of the principals in what was happening on Remington Street. I could hope that he was holed up safely in wherever the police had set up their command post, trying to get the nut with the shotgun on the phone and persuade him to throw in the towel. Jack was good at that.

"This word just in to the Channel Five studio," the anchorman said. I jerked my head up and stared at the television screen.

"The gunman who moments ago fired on police from the second-story window of a house on Remington Street in Cambridge has now been identified as thirty-four-year-old Richard Corbett Kearns. Channel Five has learned that Kearns has been sought by Cambridge police for questioning in connection with the bludgeon murder in Cambridge a week ago last Sunday of Joan Ellen Stanley, a graduate student at Harvard. We go now to Sheila McAndrew at the scene."

15

WITHOUT THINKING, I threw some money on the table, jumped up, and dashed out of Christopher's onto Mass. Avenue. An Ambassador cab was cruising by, and I waved at it frantically. The cab slowed and swerved sharply over to the curb in front of me. I yanked open the rear door, got in, and said, "Intersection of Harvard and Mass. Ave."

"By the gas station?" the cabbie asked.

"Yeah, that's it." I figured things would be easier all around if he dropped me about a block or so from Remington. The cops would be rerouting traffic from the area—not that Remington Street was a major thoroughfare—and I didn't want to chance getting caught sitting in some kind of bottleneck. Traffic in and around Harvard Square was bad enough during rush hour under normal circumstances.

The cab shot off down Mass. Avenue, nearly sideswiping a yellow Toyota. Par for the course. All Boston and Cambridge cabbies drive as if competing for the semifinals in the National Demolition Derby.

We got to the intersection of Mass. Avenue and Harvard Street without further incident. I paid the driver and was out of the cab and half running, half walking up Harvard before the car had come to a full stop. Ahead of me I could see the Channel Five news truck. A crowd had formed behind the barricades set up across the entrance to Remington. *Ghouls*, I thought, *creeps*. Then it occurred to me that I was doing exactly what I was excoriating *them* for doing.

But I had a vested interest in the outcome of what was happening on Remington Street, didn't I?

I think I was in a state of semishock. I still hadn't fully absorbed the fact that it was Richie Kearns, that cute little pathological teddy bear, who was holed up in a second-story apartment taking potshots at police and T.V. newspeople. How far gone could he be? Very, obviously, if he really thought he and his popgun had any chance whatever against fifty or so cops armed with every deadly weapon available but a cruise missile.

There were about a hundred or so people milling around behind the barricades across the top of Remington. As I approached them, I slowed down. I don't like crowds. Among other things, they make me nervous. Especially in situations like this.

On the far corner of Remington and Harvard I spotted someone I knew slightly, a reporter for the *Cambridge Chronicle*. She was leaning against the side of a green Volkswagen, scribbling furiously in a stenographer's notebook. I waited until she glanced up from her writing and then waved at her. She gave me a look of startled recognition and waved back. I walked over to her.

"What are you doing here?" she said.

"Sightseeing," I said. "Same as the rest of these good folks. Janice, *what* is going on?"

She shrugged. "Nobody seems to know, really. There's a guy with a gun up there." She pointed at the turret of the mustard-colored frame house. "He took a pot at the cops awhile ago. Didn't hit anybody, though." She glanced at me. "You know this character's a suspect in that murder last week."

"Yes, I heard," I said. "Channel Five broke *that* bit of news about fifteen minutes ago."

"Big revelation," Janice said, all the print reporter's scorn for electronic journalism heavy in her voice. She folded her arms and went back to staring at the turret room where Kearns was holed up.

"You know about Kearns, then?" I said. "I haven't seen much about him in the papers."

"The cops sort of played it down." Janice shrugged again. "But I sort of figured, you know? I mean he was Stanley's boyfriend, right? You know when a woman gets murdered the police always go after the boyfriend or the husband first."

I nodded but didn't make any comment. I was in a funny position. Janice was a police reporter—a tough, smart, aggressive one—and I wasn't too sure what else she knew about the Joan Stanley case. All that was on public record she had access to, plus whatever she could coax out of her own sources in the department. I didn't know if she knew about the missing African statue, or about the bite mark on Joan's breast. Obviously she wasn't aware that Joan and I had lived in the same building. She also didn't know about my connection with Jack. If she had she wouldn't have asked me why I was here. For some reason, I thought it best not to enlighten her on either point.

"Has anyone talked to him yet?" I asked. "Kearns?"

Janice shook her head. "Uh-uh. Cops have been trying to get him on the phone, but he won't answer."

"So what are they going to do?"

"I have no idea," she said. "Wait it out, I guess. What else can they do?" Janice removed her glasses and massaged the bridge of her nose with thumb and forefinger. "I have the feeling it's gonna be a long, cold wait, though. This Kearns must be a real basket case." She tapped her left temple. "Dippo city."

"Well, that's pretty obvious, isn't it?" I said, nodding in the direction of the house. "How many well-balanced people do you know who try to take on fifty armed cops?"

"I guess," Janice said. "God, you should have seen the panic when Kearns took that first shot."

"I did," I said. "On the television. Does anyone know why he started shooting?"

"Oh, sure. One of the cops got too close to the house. Or at least, Kearns thought he did."

I grimaced. "It's amazing *someone* didn't get blown away."

"Mmmm."

I looked up at the second floor of the turret. The window was dark, and I could discern no trace of movement in the room behind it. I wondered what Kearns was doing now, what was going through his mind. There was no way I could even begin to imagine the demons that must be driving him.

I shivered a little. It was getting terribly cold.

"Janice," I said, "who's doing the negotiating?"

She raised her eyebrows. "I'm not sure. I think maybe Marty Delgado. I saw him awhile ago, anyway. And Lingemann. You know either of them?"

"Oh, sure," I said. Marty Delgado was one of the detectives, a thin, slight young guy with a quiet, almost self-effacing manner. There was the barest trace of the Azores in his speech. He never seemed to me to be tough enough to survive in the job he had. But I knew he was highly regarded as a detective. "People tell him things," Jack had explained to me once. "They trust him." I could understand why Jack had picked Delgado for this particular task.

"Where are they doing the negotiating from?" I asked.

"You mean, where are they *trying* to do the negotiating from," Janice replied. "An apartment in the place next door." She pointed at a large

85

frame house on the corner of Harvard and Remington opposite to where we were standing. A uniformed cop stood in the doorway of the house. There was a light on in one of the first-floor rooms. The rest of the building was dark.

"Did you see Lingemann, Jan?" I said. It gave me a little jolt to refer to Jack as if he were someone with whom I only had a nodding acquaintance.

"Uh-huh," she said. "He's in there"—she jerked her head at the building on the corner—"with Delgado and some other guys I don't know." She glanced at me. "Why?"

"Just curious," I replied. The answer seemed to satisfy her, for she went back to staring at the turret room.

I didn't know whether to be relieved or disturbed that Jack was here and involved. I guess I was relieved. At least I knew *where* he was, which counted for something.

I looked down Remington Street. Bathed in the blue light from the police car flashers, it was an oddly surreal scene. The cops were poised in motionless groups of two and three, sheltered behind the cruisers. Most of them had their guns drawn and trained on the turret room. There was a sharpshooter on the roof of the building across the street from the mustard-colored frame house, and doubtless there were others like him positioned in places I couldn't see. The only sound was the occasional crackle of a radio. Even the crowd behind the barricade was subdued.

16

JANICE WAS RIGHT. It was clearly going to be a long, cold siege. And a tiring one for those of us who were determined to ride it out. Time seemed to be passing extraordinarily slowly. Perhaps it was only the relative absence of movement and sound on Remington Street. The cops remained frozen in their places, watchful and silent, like the Indian scouts in old Westerns. The tension in the air was as dense and nearly as visible as fog.

After a while I grew hungry, despite the knot of apprehension in my stomach. Usually when I'm nervous I lose my appetite. Maybe it wasn't food I needed now—just something to do. I asked Janice if she wanted anything to eat. She said yes, so I walked down to a take-out restaurant on Mass. Avenue and got some coffee and sandwiches to go. On the way back to Remington Street I glanced up at the clock on the top of the Cambridge Savings Bank. It was only ten. It felt more like three A.M.

The crowd at the intersection of Harvard and Remington had nearly doubled in size. If for some reason it got out of hand, the cops were going to have one hell of a mess on their hands. I studied some of the faces. Nobody, happily, looked especially violent or excitable. There were a lot of studenty-looking types in jeans and down parkas, standing around in small groups and chatting with each other. Taking a break from the calculus and poli sci and chemistry homework, I figured. Then it dawned on me that a considerable number of them might live on Remington—this was a big student neighborhood—and that maybe most of them were just hanging out waiting to be allowed back into their apartments. Oh, well. They'd all have dynamite excuses for not being prepared for classes tomorrow.

Sorry I can't hand in my paper, Professor Smith. I was gonna type it last night, but when I tried to get into my apartment a crazy guy threatened to shoot me.

I gave Janice her sandwich and coffee, and we sat down on the curb to eat.

"Anything happen while I was gone?" I asked.

Janice took a bite of her sandwich and shook her head. "Not much. Still no word from Kearns, as far as I can tell. I think the cops are starting to get a little antsy."

The police weren't the only ones getting fidgety. "Couldn't they force him out?" I said, looking up at Kearns's darkened turret room.

Janice glanced at me. "How?"

"Well, I don't know." I shrugged. "There ought to be something they can do. Start lobbing tear gas canisters through the windows maybe?"

Janice shook her head again. "Too risky."

I thought for a moment. "Could somebody slip in through the back of the house?"

She laughed. "And do what?"

"Distract Kearns? Or sneak up on him and grab the gun?"

"You've been watching too much television," she said. "It doesn't work that way. Anyway it's too early for them to try anything drastic. They'll wait. As long as Kearns doesn't start shooting again."

I sighed. "So what will happen?"

"I don't know," she replied. "I've been to a lot of things like this. If they can get Kearns to talk to them, they have at least a chance of wrapping things up without anybody getting hurt. If not . . . I don't know *what* will happen."

I finished my sandwich and wiped my hands on a paper napkin. Then I stood up. "I'm going to walk around for a while," I said. "I'm too restless to sit still."

Janice nodded. "Talk to you later," she said. "Thanks for the food."

"My pleasure," I said, and moved away. Janice resumed eating and staring at the turret room.

I wandered through the crowd, occasionally eavesdropping on those groups of people who looked to be having the liveliest conversations. The rumor mill was working overtime tonight. I overheard a fat girl in pigtails telling two other kids that the guy with the shotgun was a major league dope dealer. I listened to someone else speculate that Kearns was a convicted multiple murderer recently escaped from Walpole. Nobody seemed to have the story completely straight. Which was kind of funny in view of the fact that every tenth person in the crowd was probably either a newspaper or T.V. reporter.

I tried to imagine what Jack must be doing now. How long would it take him to get Kearns on the phone? And when he did, what would the two of them talk about? The weather? What teams would make the Superbowl? Imported versus domestic beers? Soybean futures?

Jack had once described to me some of the conversations he'd had with people who'd done what Kearns was doing. The thing that struck me most was how mundane, even trivial, the subjects of these chats always turned out to be. Some wild-eyed, foaming-at-the-mouth, gun-toting fanatic would start out screaming that he was going to blow away everyone in sight, including the cops. Jack would get the guy on the phone and try to calm him down. That always took a while. Then, after his initial hysteria had passed, the guy would start making lots of demands. Bizarre ones, in some cases. Sometimes he'd insist on safe passage to Nicaragua. Sometimes he'd want a guest shot on the eleven o'clock news. Jack would talk around all these imperatives, making no concessions and no denials. Slowly, the guy would decide that for a pig, Jack wasn't all that bad. They'd start to talk about personal things. The guy would tell Jack his problems and grievances. Jack would commiserate with him. After that, it was usually only a matter of more time till the guy surrendered.

"How do you do it?" I'd asked Jack. "How do you get them to give it up? What's the trick?"

"No trick," he'd replied. "It's simple. They get so bored listening to me that after a while they start to figure that *anything* has to be better."

Sometimes, of course, the situation didn't go that way.

I wondered if tonight would turn out to be one of the exceptions to the rule.

How long could Kearns continue to stay in that darkened room, refusing to answer the phone, his shotgun leveled at the cops in the street below? Would he crack, finally? And if so, what would he do beforehand? Kill someone? Confess to the murder of Joan Stanley?

Jack, I knew, would be willing to sit for however long it took to establish contact with Kearns. But suppose such a thing never happened? What would he do then?

I rubbed my face and leaned wearily against the side of somebody's Volvo station wagon. It was a little past midnight. I was exhausted, yet wired to the teeth, a truly lousy combination of sensations. How was Jack feeling? Probably a hell of a lot calmer than I. He always was, at least on the outside.

Out of the corner of my eye, I caught a flash of movement on Remington Street. I looked up, massaging the back of my neck. A plainclothes cop had come out of the house on the corner and was heading toward one of the cruisers. I pushed myself away from the side of the Volvo and walked over to Janice. She was deep in conversation with one of the uniformed guys. I waited till they'd finished talking and then went up to her.

"What's happening?" I said.

"They got through to Kearns," she replied.

I widened my eyes. "*Really?*" I said. "Hey, that's great."

"Maybe."

I looked at her quizzically. "Huh? What's the matter?"

She shook her head. "He's completely off his rocker. Says if the cops aren't all cleared out in the next five minutes, he's going to start shooting."

At that moment, one of the cruisers started up and began backing slowly down Remington. The street was too narrow to allow for a U turn. Another cruiser pulled away from the curb.

"My God," I said, staring at it. "They're not leaving, just like that, are they?" I snapped my fingers. "They can't just pick up and leave."

"No, of course not," Janice replied. She nodded at the two cruisers moving down Remington. "That's just for effect."

"You think Kearns will buy it?" I asked skeptically. "How dumb can he be?"

Janice shrugged. "Delaying tactic. Anyway Kearns probably isn't thinking too straight just now."

"That's true," I said. I glanced up at the roof of the building behind me. The sharpshooter was crouched beside the chimney, statue-still and deadly. I wondered what was going through *his* mind.

"If they can keep Kearns on the phone . . ." Janice said. She didn't bother to finish the sentence. She didn't have to.

I turned up the collar on my jacket and stuffed my hands in my pockets. I was freezing cold and I had desperately to go to the bathroom. Six hours, I thought. Six hours it had taken them to establish contact with Kearns.

I'd read about situations like this that had dragged on for days.

The crowd was aware that something had happened, even if it didn't know what. Some of the people had moved forward and were pressed up against the barricades. I looked at them and felt a prickle of unease. It was like waiting for a cattle stampede to break loose.

I glanced over to where the television news folks had congregated. Sheila McAndrew, the woman from Channel Five, was talking with her cameraman. Occasionally she'd break off to point at the mustard-colored frame house. The cameraman would nod in agreement. Probably he and she were planning how best to capture the big surrender scene on film.

A reporter from Channel Four was interviewing people in the crowd. I backed off, out of his range. I tend to be camera and microphone shy.

I was bending over to retie a shoelace when there was a muffled bang from inside the mustard-colored frame house. I looked up quickly. A cop standing about ten feet from me said, "Oh, *shit*." The crowd gave a sort of collective murmuring sigh, and those in front pressed up closer against the barricades. The wooden sawhorse before them swayed and nearly toppled over. One of the crowd control patrolmen grabbed it and steadied it. He yelled something at the people standing nearest him and they moved back marginally.

I got up and walked over to where Janice was standing. "That was a shot, wasn't it?" I said.

She nodded.

"Kearns," I said.

"Uh-huh."

We stared at the frame house. A cop wearing a flak jacket and carrying a shotgun edged around past the porch and vanished behind an overgrown yew.

"They're going to go in after him, aren't they?" I said.

"Looks like it, doesn't it?" Janice rubbed her hands together and blew on them. "God, I wish I had another cup of that coffee. I'd stick my feet in it. I can't feel my damn toes." She stamped up and down to underscore the point.

At that moment, Jack and Marty Delgado and another pair of cops I didn't recognize came out of the house on the corner. They walked in silent file across the skinny strip of front lawn to Kearns's place, turned, and merged with the shadows at the side of the building. They, too, had shotguns. Shotguns seemed to be the evening's weapon of choice. I wondered if Kearns were watching them from his turret window. I shivered and took my hands out of my pockets and pulled my coat tighter around me.

"What's the matter?" Janice asked.

I shook my head vigorously. "Nothing. It's cold." I wanted to run up to the nearest cop and grab him by the arm and shake him and demand that he tell me exactly what was going on.

A light flashed on in the turret room. There was another chorus of murmurs from the crowd. Louder, this time.

"Ooohhh," Janice said softly. "They must be inside. God, that was quick, wasn't it?"

"Uh-huh," I said. I was holding myself rigid, braced for another blast of gunfire.

Perhaps five or so minutes passed. Then the front door of the frame house opened and a man stepped out on the porch. He was backlit by the illumination from the entranceway and for a moment was nothing more than a tall silhouette. I squinted. The man descended the porch steps. It was Jack. I closed my eyes and let out a long breath.

Jack came down the short path from the house to the sidewalk. He was walking slowly, his head slightly bent, almost as if he didn't care to risk glancing up and catching anyone else's eye. I watched him very carefully. Even from a distance, he looked unutterably weary. Weary and something else. Defeated? Dejected?

Lieutenant De Christo met him at the gate. Jack spoke to him briefly and De Christo shook his head. Jack shrugged and leaned against the gatepost. Then a flock of reporters converged on him and I lost sight of him altogether.

Something bad had taken place up in that turret room.

The ambulance attendants had opened the rear doors of the ambulance and were pulling from it a wheeled stretcher. They set it on the ground and began rolling it across the street to the frame house.

Jack broke free of the throng of reporters and walked over to one of the police cruisers. He was still holding the shotgun, I noticed. He unloaded the thing and handed it to one of the uniformed cops. He dropped the shells in his pocket, turned, and started walking back down Remington Street in the direction of Mass. Avenue, away from the crowd. I launched myself after him.

I had to trot to catch up. When I was about ten feet behind him, I halted and said, "Jack."

"Yeah?" he said, without breaking stride or even looking back.

"It's me," I said.

This time he paused. He turned and looked at me blankly for several seconds. Then he shook his head a little and said, "What are you doing here?"

The question was so stupid that I didn't bother to answer it. Instead, I went up to him and put my hand on his arm. "Are you okay?" I asked.

"Yeah, I'm fine."

"Good. Can I come along with you?"

He nodded. I put my hand through his arm and we resumed walking down Remington, past a large brick apartment building and an auto body shop.

"Where are we going?" I said.

"No place," he replied.

We got to the corner of Remington and Mass. Avenue and stopped. I looked up at him.

92

"Jack," I said. "What happened back there?"

He was silent for a moment, gazing at me. Then he said, "Kearns is dead."

"Oh, my God," I said. "How?"

"He shot himself."

"Oh, *no*."

Jack looked away from me and down Mass. Avenue. "He put that god-damned gun in his mouth and blew off his head."

"Oh, God," I repeated, sickened.

Jack kicked at a beer can on the sidewalk and sent it clattering into the gutter. "Shit," he burst out. "Shit, shit, shit."

17

SOME OF THE questions I'd had about Richie Kearns got answered right away. The others took a little longer.

The woman who owned the mustard-colored frame house on Remington Street—but didn't live there herself—swore up and down that she'd never seen Kearns before and that, furthermore, she'd had no idea the second floor turret apartment was even occupied. The previous tenant, somebody named Stephen Dalferro, had moved out at the end of October. The landlady had no notion where he'd gone. She was planning to renovate the apartment, raise the rent a hundred bucks, and put it back on the market in December. She couldn't say how Kearns had gained access to the building.

That little mystery was solved in relatively short order. Jack put out a trace on Dalferro and tracked him down to Fresno, California, where he had a job with the Department of Human Resources. Dalferro told the Fresno cops that, yes, he'd known Kearns while they'd been students in the education department at Harvard. They'd been fairly friendly, had gone out for a beer after classes sometimes. No, Dalferro had never met Joan Stanley. No, he hadn't heard that she was dead, and that Richie was a prime suspect in her murder. No, he didn't know about Richie's psychological problems. Yes, he thought he knew how Kearns had gotten into the apartment on Remington Street.

Dalferro had spent the first two weeks of September traveling around the country on various job interviews. He had a cat, which he obviously couldn't take along with him on the trip. The cat hated travel and new environments anyway. Kearns had volunteered to feed it and keep its litter box changed while Dalferro was away. Dalferro had lent him a spare set of keys so that Richie could get in and out of the place on Remington Street, which had no resident superintendent. When Dalferro had returned from his trip, he'd completely forgotten to ask Richie to give back the keys.

Apparently Kearns hadn't been holed up in Dalferro's apartment for very long. Jack told me that none of the building's other tenants had heard a sound from the place until late Monday afternoon. At about five-thirty one of the second-floor residents, returning home from work, had noticed a flicker of light in the turret window of Dalferro's apartment. Since she'd known the apartment had been vacant for several weeks, she'd assumed that maybe a new tenant was moving in there. Her curiosity aroused, she'd gone over and knocked on the door. Kearns had screamed at her to go away, he had a gun. The woman had run back to her own apartment and called the police. Then she'd raced around the building to warn the other tenants.

Where Kearns had been staying before he'd turned up in the house on Remington Street, we could only guess. But there were some good indicators. When he and the other detectives were going through Dalferro's apartment afterward, Jack had found a half-empty box of Marlboros with a New Hampshire tax stamp on it. In Kearns's wallet was a cash register slip from a grocery store in Laconia, New Hampshire. The register slip dated from the previous Friday.

Kearns's own apartment on Huron Avenue showed no signs of recent occupancy, which surprised no one. There was also nothing in it to suggest that Kearns had been in any way involved in Joan's death, which surprised a few people. No bloody clothes stuffed in a plastic bag and hidden in the back of a closet. No object that might conceivably have been used as a weapon.

Kearns didn't have the African statue that had disappeared from Joan's apartment, either.

But so what? If I had murdered someone, the first thing I'd do would be to get rid of the weapon I'd used to commit the crime. Perhaps Kearns had done the same thing. Wacked-out as he was, he was probably capable of performing *some* rational actions.

I was beginning to tend very strongly toward the belief that it had, in fact, been Richie who'd murdered Joan. If the people in the medical examiner's office could ever reassemble enough of Kearns's jaw to make an impression of his bite, they could compare it to the bite mark on Joan's breast and prove me right.

It occurred to me, in a mood of ironic detachment, that I now had the denouement to the story I wanted to write about the death of Joan Stanley.

I was feeling somewhat differently about things than Jack was. It took him a day or so to snap out of the depression he'd fallen into after the events of Monday evening. I could understand something of what he felt. Not all of it, though. We talked about this a little bit Tuesday evening, after dinner at my house.

"It wasn't your fault," I said, for the third or fourth time. "The man was crazy. There was no way you or anyone else could have stopped him from doing what he did."

"I know that," Jack replied. "I'm not blaming myself for anything."

"But it still bothers you."

"Sure."

"Why?"

He shook his head. "*That* I don't know. It didn't—it ended the wrong way, I guess."

I picked up my coffee cup. "And the right way would have been if you or Marty Delgado or somebody else had been able to talk Richie into throwing down the shotgun and giving himself up."

"Well, yes, of course." Jack shrugged. "But it didn't happen that way, so it's pointless to keep going over and over the thing."

"Okay," I said. "I'll drop the subject. I don't like to see you depressed, that's all."

He smiled a little. "I'll get over it."

"I know that," I said. I reached over and patted his arm. "Look, why don't you go in the living room and build a fire while I clean up the dishes? When I get done I'll join you and we can listen to records or watch television or something thrilling like that."

"Suppose there's nothing good on T.V.," he said.

"Then maybe we can come up with another way of passing the time," I said, smiling.

"Yeah, I'll give it some thought," he said. He left the kitchen and I started transferring the dirty dishes from the table to the sink. There was a smidgen of leftover lasagna in the baking dish, not enough to be worth saving, so I gave it to Lucy.

I rinsed the wineglasses and propped them up on the drainer. Then I dried my hands on the dish towel and went to the living room door. There was a nice little blaze crackling away in the fireplace. Jack was going through the books in the bookcase. He picked one out entitled *Celtic Britain*, by Nora K. Chadwick, opened it, and began reading the blurb on the dust jacket flap. He didn't notice me standing in the doorway. I smiled to myself and went back to the kitchen.

The last time I'd been to the New Hampshire State Liquor Store, I'd bought a bottle of applejack. I got it from the cupboard, set it on a tray with two brandy snifters, and carried it into the living room. Jack was lying on the floor in front of the fireplace, engrossed in *Celtic Britain*. I set the tray on the coffee table and said, "Surprise."

He looked up, startled. "I didn't hear you come in."

"I could tell," I said. I nodded at the book. "What're you reading about? Boudicca and the revolt of the Iceni?"

"Uh-huh." He got up and came over to the couch and sat down next to me. He looked at the bottle of applejack and said, "What's this?"

"My latest taste sensation," I replied. "Want some?"

"Sure."

I poured us each a glass. I picked mine up, made a little salutory gesture with it, and said, "Here's to homicide."

He laughed and put his arm around me.

We sat without talking for quite some while, sipping our drinks and watching the fire. Lucy padded into the room and lay down alongside the coffee table. Some music would have been nice, but I felt too languid to get up and put a record on the stereo. Also I didn't want to move and dislodge Jack's arm from my shoulder. I wondered, idly, if this was what it was like to be married. Somehow the notion didn't seem as appalling to me as it once had. Maybe I was getting old. Maybe Jack was. I shook my head and laughed a little. I'm thirty-three. Jack's forty-one.

"What's funny?" Jack asked.

"Nothing," I said. "Random thought." I set my glass on the coffee table. "Jack, before it slips my mind. I have a box of Joan's stuff. Maybe you ought to take a look at it."

His eyebrows went up. "What's in it?"

I shrugged. "Haven't the vaguest notion. Here, let me get it." I got up and went to the living room closet, where I'd put the box after Peter Lewis had dropped it off Sunday afternoon. I dragged the box out from behind some boots and pushed it with my foot over to the sofa.

The box had been sealed with packing tape. Jack reached into his pocket, took out a small folding knife, opened it, and ran the blade beneath the flaps of the box. I sat down next to him on the couch.

"Where'd this stuff come from?" Jack said.

"Joan's office," I replied. "Peter Lewis dropped it off the other day."

Jack folded the knife and put it back in his pocket. "Lewis was here?" he asked.

"Yes," I said. "For about fifteen minutes Sunday afternoon." I gestured at the box. "He and some of the other people at the crisis center were cleaning out Joan's office, and they weren't sure what to do with her stuff. So Lewis brought it over here and I told him I'd keep it for when her family came to pack up the things from her apartment."

"Uh-huh," Jack said. "Well, ya never know what'll turn out to be useful." He was leaning over the box, peeling off the tape. There was an abstracted expression on what I could see of his face. Treasure hunter.

He stripped off the last of the tape, rolled it up into a ball, and dropped it on the coffee table. Then he bent back the flaps of the box. I slid off the couch and knelt on the floor next to the container. "Hmmm. Doesn't look too fascinating, contentswise, does it?" I remarked.

Jack reached into the box and took from it two books. One was on family therapy and the other on sexual deviance. He set them on the coffee table. I picked up the one on sexual deviance and flipped through it. It fell open to a section headed "Frottage." I read through the passage and started to giggle. There's some part of me that's forever a sixth-grader, equating prurience with hilarity. Oh, well. Judging from the well-thumbed look of that particular page of the book, Joan and her colleagues had derived some chuckles from what was printed on it as well.

"What is it?" Jack asked. He removed a chipped blue ceramic mug and a green wirebound notebook from the box.

"Are you familiar with the term *frotteur*?" I said.

He glanced up at me quickly, looking a little startled, and then, slowly, started to grin.

"I see you are," I said. "Not from personal experience, I hope."

"Are you kidding," he said. "That's how I get my rocks off."

"By rubbing up against women in the subway?" I said. "Charming." I shut the book with a snap and set it on the coffee table. "So, Lieutenant Frotteur," I said. "What else is in Pandora's box?"

He shook his head. "Nothing that looks as if it means anything. Mostly books and notebooks. Still, I'll take it with me."

"Sure," I said. "Be my guest." I got up and climbed back next to him on the couch. "Want another drink?"

He started repacking the box. "Okay. That stuff's not bad."

"Grows on you," I agreed, pouring us each another glass of applejack.

"Mmmm," Jack said. He leaned back against the couch cushions and draped his arm around me. "Sort of like a taste for frottage."

18

WHEN I GOT up late Wednesday morning, it was snowing, the first time for that season. The flakes were the huge puffy kind that seem to fall in slow motion and usually melt on contact with the ground. Today they weren't. Perhaps an inch of snow had accumulated—not enough to plow, but enough to make the streets slick and sloppy-looking. I sat in the bowed-out living room window for a while watching the kids across the way try to build what I guessed was an igloo. Then I went to make myself some breakfast.

There was a note from Jack on the kitchen table. I read it over, smiled, and tucked it into my bathrobe pocket.

I put some water on for coffee. While I was waiting for the kettle to boil, I had some grapefruit juice and rye toast. When the coffee was made I poured a cup and took it back to the living room. The dog was sacked out full-length on the couch, snoring happily away and giving new meaning to the word "flaccid." I gave her a swat on the rump and said, "Move it." Reluctantly, she made room for me. I got settled with my coffee and turned on the radio, just in time to catch the last few bars of an Olivia Newton-John ditty about a heart attack. Great subject for a song. There was a commercial for the Suffolk Franklin Savings Bank, a time tone, and an irritatingly orotund male voice said, "Good morning. This is Charles Greenhow with the WCSK eleven o'clock report. The body of twenty-one-year-old Sandra Dembkoski was discovered early this morning by a relative in Ms. Dembkoski's first-floor apartment on Franklin Street in Cambridge. Ms. Dembkoski, who was found lying in bed, had apparently been beaten to death. Police have so far refused to comment on any similarities between this slaying and the bludgeon murder ten days ago of twenty-four-year-old Joan Stanley, also a Cambridge resident. No arrests have been made in either case. Renewed fighting has broken out on the border of . . ."

I reached over and snapped off the radio. Then I sat perfectly still for perhaps thirty seconds, feeling stunned and slightly sickened. My first impulse was to call Jack. I even reached reflexively for the phone. Then it occurred to me that my chances of getting through to him were probably nil. The switchboard at the station was probably lit up like the Christmas tree at Rockefeller Center. If I wanted to talk to him, I'd have better luck if I just went down to the station and hung around till he had a free moment.

Police have so far refused to comment on any similarities between this slaying and the bludgeon murder ten days ago of twenty-four-year-old Joan Stanley.

I knew the real meaning of that kind of official equivocation. Maybe I *didn't* yet have the denouement to the story I wanted to write about Joan's death.

I took a fast shower and dressed in jeans, the heaviest sweater I owned, boots, and a pile-lined windbreaker. Then I hustled Lucy outside for a very short walk. She was enchanted with the snow and wanted to play, but I hauled her back inside after five minutes. I think she was annoyed with me. Tough.

I decided to walk to the police station. The snow was coming down harder now, and it was slippery underfoot, so the hike wouldn't be especially pleasant. But I didn't have much choice. The bus service in my part of Cambridge is sporadic at best, and in poor weather, it seems to be nonexistent. There'd be a wait for a cab.

It took me a little over an hour to mush my way to Central Square. Normally, the walk took about half as much time.

The police station, when I got there, was mobbed. It looked very much the way it had the night Joan Stanley had died. There were reporters crawling all over the place. Some of them were draped over the desk, chivying the cops working the phones. Others were standing around in small groups, conversing animatedly with each other. It was like a press convention. The desk sergeant, a big burly guy with a toper's red bulbous nose, was wandering through the crowd shaking his head and looking disgusted.

I spotted Janice Miller, the crime reporter from the *Cambridge Chronicle*, sitting on the end of the long oak bench in the waiting area. I picked my way over to her.

"You again," she said. "What is this? You stringing for the *Herald* or what?"

"Not hardly," I said, yanking off my ski hat and shaking about two pounds of snow from it.

"Well, what, then?" she said. "You're not a crime writer."

100

I laughed. "I seem to have become one recently."

"Huh?"

"*Cambridge Monthly* asked me to do a story on Joan Stanley."

"What the hell for?" Janice asked.

I shrugged. "They thought it would make an interesting feature. You know—one of those none-of-us-is-safe-from-violent-crime-anymore jobs. Brandon Peters loves that kind of crap."

Janice shook her head. "I thought all *Cambridge Monthly* was interested in was where you could buy the best chocolate chip cookies in town."

"They're growing a social conscience," I replied.

"Goody for them," Janice said.

"They pay me," I said. "They can advocate Rosicrucianism for all I care. What do you hear about the woman who got murdered last night?" I tilted my head at the throng of reporters. "I assume that's why you're all here."

"Uh-huh," Janice said. She looked at her watch. "There's supposed to be a press conference in an hour."

"Oh? Who's talking?"

"The chief."

I nodded. "This is a bad one, isn't it?"

Janice rolled her eyes. "You're telling me? You know that woman got murdered the exact same way Stanley did."

"I guessed that," I said. "Do you know any of the details?"

"Well, some. This Dembkoski was apparently beaten over the head with something heavy and sharp."

I winced. "What else?"

Janice sighed and scratched her chin. "They're pretty sure she was raped."

"And?"

"That's all I know."

I nodded, not trusting myself to say anything further. If I did, I might inadvertently give away something Janice wasn't supposed to know. Jack has always trusted my discretion. I didn't want to give him a reason to regret he had.

"It's ironic," Janice said.

"What is?"

"Oh, just that I'm pretty sure the cops thought they had the Stanley thing wrapped up when Kearns blew his brains out. I mean, he was such an obvious suspect and all. But now . . ."

"Well," I began cautiously, "Kearns still could have murdered Joan, you know. This latest could just be the work of another cuckoo. You've heard of imitative crime, Jan."

"Oh, sure," she said. "I don't know, though. I have a feeling that Stanley and Dembkoski got murdered by the same guy. I mean, how many sex killers do we have running around Cambridge at any one given time? It's not that big a city."

"True," I said. "But per capita, it's probably got more flakes on the loose than Los Angeles."

"Wait and see," Janice said. "I bet I'm right."

"Say you are," I said. "Say Dembkoski and Stanley were murdered by the same man. How did he happen to hit on those two? What's the connection between them? Did they know each other?"

"That I couldn't tell you," Janice said. "Maybe the chief'll enlighten us at the press conference."

"Yeah," I said. I brushed my hair back from my forehead. "Have you heard anything at all about Dembkoski?"

"A little," Janice said.

"Like what," I said.

Janice glanced at me sideways, a little grin on her face. "Weeelll," she drawled. "The word is that Ms. Dembkoski was what my mother would have called a floozie."

I stared at her. "A prostitute?"

"Not quite," Janice said. "Let's just say Ms. Dembkoski was a habitué of the bars and leave it at that."

"Oh," I said. "Well, what did she do when she wasn't getting loaded and picking up guys?"

"Worked in the typing pool at one of the insurance companies. John Hancock, I think."

I nodded. "Well, so far I can't see much connection between her and Joan Stanley. Can you?"

"No," Janice admitted. "But you never know what'll come out in the wash. Right?"

"Right," I said. I stood up. "Jan, excuse me a moment. I gotta find the ladies' room."

"There's one down the end of the hall to the right," she said.

"Thanks. I'll find it." I backed off into the throng of reporters. In doing so, I nearly fell over the desk sergeant. He grabbed me by the elbow and steadied me.

"I beg your pardon," I said.

"Yeah," he said. "Whyn't you all go find a nice fire to cover?"

I made my way to the stairs, looked over my shoulder to make sure none of the reporters were watching, and then darted up the steps. When I got to the second floor I was winded. I leaned against the corridor wall outside the office of the chief's secretary, trying to catch my breath.

Jack came out of the chief's office and stopped dead when he saw me.

"Hi," I said.

"Hi," he said.

"Can we talk?" I said.

"Not here. Come on."

We went up another flight of stairs to his office in the Criminal Investigation Division.

"What's it like downstairs?" Jack asked.

"Wild," I said. "An A. J. Liebling Festival."

He shook his head. "What are they saying?"

I repeated to him what Janice had told me.

"Well, they've got it right as far as it goes," he said. We went into his office. Jack sat down behind the desk. I took the chair across from him and shrugged out of my windbreaker.

"I only have a minute," he said.

"I know," I said. I looked at him. "Is it true?"

"Is what true?"

"That whoever killed that girl last night also killed Joan?"

He hesitated a moment, then sighed deeply and said, "It looks that way. I can't say for certain till the lab tests come back, but, yes, it looks that way."

"There was a bite mark on her?" I said. "Same place? Same kind of impression?"

"Well, it looked that way to me."

"Oh, God."

"Everything was the same, as far as I can see," Jack continued. "Whoever it was who did it, didn't break into her apartment. There weren't any signs of forced entry on the door or windows." He leaned back in the chair and clasped his hands behind his head. "Oh, yeah. There was blood in the bathtub. Not much."

I made a face. "I *still* think that's the most revolting part of the whole thing. How the guy cleans up after himself."

"Uh-huh."

I was silent for a moment, chewing on my lower lip. Then I said, "Jack?"

"Yes?"

"That was what was bothering you last night, wasn't it? You never really believed that Richie killed Joan, did you?"

He made a slight shrugging gesture with one shoulder.

"No, you didn't," I said. I took a deep breath and let it out very slowly. "And you were right."

He didn't say anything. The radiator in the corner made a hissing noise. From the street there were muffled traffic sounds.

"I guess I should go now," I said, after a moment. "Let you get back to work." I started putting on my windbreaker.

"There's something else," Jack said.

I paused, one arm halfway into the sleeve of my jacket. "Oh?"

"That girl last night," Jack said. He shook his head. "I knew who she was." He looked at me. "You did, too, in a way."

I frowned at him. "I did? How?"

"Remember last week when you met me for a drink at that place on Brattle Street?"

"Sure I remember." I smiled. "I walked in and caught you *in flagrante delicto* with that poor silly little drunken blonde." The last word out of my mouth ended in a kind of shocked exhalation. "Oh, God, no," I said. "*Her*? That girl who was all over you? *That* was Sandra Dembkoski?"

"Uh-huh."

19

"My God," I repeated softly. I felt as if I'd been kicked in the solar plexus.

The phone on the desk rang. Jack picked up the receiver and said, "Yes?"

Mechanically, I finished shrugging into my windbreaker. Then I rose.

"Yeah," Jack was saying into the phone. "Yeah, okay." He was silent for a few seconds. "All right, good." He paused again. "Yeah."

There was a memo pad on the desk blotter. I leaned over, took a sheet from the pad, and with Jack's pen scrawled "See you later" on it. I pushed the paper across the desk with my fingertips until it was squarely in front of him. He glanced down at it, then up at me, and nodded. I raised my hand to him and left the office. As I went out the door I heard him say, "No, I'll take care of it."

I walked downstairs in something of a daze and shouldered my way through the throng of cops and reporters to the door. Janice Miller was where I'd left her, parked on the bench in the waiting area. She was talking to a man from the *Herald*. I waved to her and hurried out the station door before she could call to me. I wanted to get away by myself and think for a while.

Events were moving too quickly for me to grasp.

The storm appeared to be assuming blizzard proportions. What little traffic there was had slowed to a crawl, and over Central Square there hung that hush that is peculiar to city landscapes under snow cover. Head bent against the wind, I walked up Western Avenue, turned right onto Mass. Avenue, and trudged another two blocks till I came to a sandwich shop. I went in. The place was deserted except for the counterman. He looked thrilled to see another human being. We exchanged comments about the weather as he poured me some coffee.

I took my cup to a window table and sat down, staring out at the swirling white blankness of Mass. Avenue.

What the hell kind of butcher did we have running around Cambridge? And how many more women would he kill before the cops caught him?

I sat in the coffee shop till a little past three, when the manager wanted to close up because of the weather. The police department press conference must already have been held. I wondered if the chief had made any startling revelations about Dembkoski's murder to the assembled reporters. Probably not. If he had, I'd hear about them in detail from Jack. But what the hell, startling or otherwise, could there be to reveal at this stage of the investigation? The detectives were probably as much in the dark as the reporters. Maybe.

Police work has a number of axioms. One of them is that murder investigations, unless the cops catch the murderer practically standing over the body holding a smoking gun, almost always seem hopeless at the beginning. Another axiom is that the more time that passes without a solution to a case, the more hopeless the case will seem.

I paid for my coffee and left the restaurant. Then I mushed my way back to the police station. As I'd figured, the press conference was in the process of breaking up. I saw Janice Miller standing at the foot of the stairs with a couple of other reporters. I waved to her. She broke away from her group and hustled over to me.

"Where'd you disappear to?" she demanded.

"Get some coffee," I replied. "Why? Did I miss anything good?"

She shrugged. "Nothing amazing. Some more background on Dembkoski. Plus the usual stuff about the cops pursuing several promising leads. Although they never tell you what the leads are."

"I've noted that," I said. We strolled over to the bench in the waiting area and sat down. The desk sergeant walked past us. He was looking a lot happier now that the crowd of reporters was beginning to disperse.

"So what's the story with Sandra Dembkoski?" I asked.

"Why should I share my findings with you?" Janice replied.

"Oh, knock it off," I said. "Everything the chief told you people will be on the public record. If I don't get it from you, I'll get it from somebody else."

She laughed. "Okay. Let's see." She removed a stenographer's notebook from her shoulder bag and flipped it open in her lap. "Let's see," she repeated. She ran her finger down a page covered with cramped, tiny handwriting. "Right. Sandra Dembkoski, born in Dorchester. Graduated from Jamaica Plain High three years ago last June. Youngest of three sisters. The other two are married and live out of state. The father's deceased. The mother still lives in Jamaica Plain. On Sedgewick Street. Sandra moved to Cambridge two years ago. Over her mother's objections, I understand."

"She should have listened to her mother," I said.

"Yeah," Janice said. She reached into her coat pocket and extracted a linty-looking tissue and blew her nose on it.

"So what else?" I prompted.

"About Dembkoski?" Janice asked. She crumpled the tissue and looked around for a wastebasket to toss it into. Finding none, she shoved it back into her coat pocket. "Well, the chief kind of avoided the specifics—maybe he doesn't like to speak ill of the dead or something—but I got the very distinct impression that what I told you before about Sandra being a bit of a tramp was exactly right."

"Oh?" I said. There formed in my mind a vivid picture of a blond girl in red satin blouse and black slacks leaning over Jack and whispering something into his ear, and him smiling and shaking his head.

"Mmmm," Janice said. "Old Sandra seems to have led an active and diverse social life. With about half the nongay male population of Cambridge. At one time or another."

I grimaced.

"What's wrong?" Janice asked.

"Oh, nothing." I sighed. "It's just that—how does anyone her age get to be such a mess so fast?"

Janice snorted, or maybe it was only her sinuses. "Sandra was hardly unique in that respect, you know."

"I know," I said. "That's the depressing part." I shook my head.

"Anyway," Janice said. "Like I told you before, she worked in the typing pool at John Hancock. Had a series of jobs before that. After she graduated from high school she started with New England Life as a receptionist. Stayed there for about a year, then went over to the State Street Bank, doing I don't know what. Apparently she didn't like it too well there, either, or they didn't like her, 'cause she left them after about six months. Collected unemployment for a while, then got a job as a typist in the psych department at Harvard—"

"Holy shit," I said.

Janice looked at me in astonishment. "What's the matter with you?"

"That's the connection," I said.

"Huh?"

"The connection," I repeated. "The one between Stanley and Dembkoski. Joan was a graduate student in the Harvard psych department."

Janice's eyes widened. "Jesus. I didn't even think of that. My God. You're right."

We stared at each other for a few seconds, not saying anything. My mind was racing. Janice was frowning a little, as if trying to puzzle something out.

"It's one hell of a coincidence," she said finally. "But does it mean anything? I mean, lots of people work in the same place, you know?"

"Yeah," I said. I deliberated for a moment. "Jan?"

"Yes?"

"Do you know if Sandra worked for anyone in particular while she was at Harvard? I mean, any particular professor?"

She gave me a sharp, curious look. "Why?"

I shook my head. "You tell me what I want to know, and then I'll explain why it's important."

She gazed at me for a moment and then nodded. "Okay. I'll check. Hold on a minute." She got up and went over to the pay phone. I watched her as she dropped a coin into the box and dialed a number. There was a small pause and she began speaking into the mouthpiece, too softly for me to overhear. After about two minutes had passed, she hung up the phone and came back to me.

"Well?" I said.

"She worked for a couple of professors. Typing their notes and articles and syllabuses and crap like that."

"A couple of professors," I echoed. "Did you get their names?"

"Uh-huh."

"Okay. Was one of them a guy called Christopher Bingham?"

"Yeah," Janice said, sounding surprised. "How'd you guess that?"

"It's not important," I said hastily. "Doesn't the name mean anything to you?"

Janice looked thoughtful. "Bingham," she murmured. "Bingham, Bingham." She shook her head. "Nope. Not a thing. Should it?"

"Goddam," I said. "Harvard can cover up anything. If a neutron bomb went off in the Yard, they'd figure out a way to keep it quiet."

Janice scowled at me and said, "What the *hell* are you babbling about?"

I bit my lip. "Jan," I said. "I'm going to tell you something you're not supposed to know. You gotta promise me you'll keep it to yourself for— oh, a day, at least? The whole thing will probably have blown up by then."

"I can't promise anything until I know what it is," she replied.

"Oh, God," I said. "All right. Christopher Bingham was Joan Stanley's dissertation adviser. He was also her lover. She was hassling him about getting a divorce from his wife and marrying her."

Janice's mouth dropped open in astonishment.

108

"I can't believe you didn't know," I said. "I thought maybe the cops had asked you to keep it quiet or something."

"Like hell," Janice said. "Nobody ever said anything about it to me. Not to any of the other writers, either, as far as I can tell."

"You didn't go over to the psych department to interview anyone there?" I asked incredulously.

"Well, sure," Janice replied. "I talked to a couple people. But all they said was what a nice person Joan was and what a terrible tragedy the whole thing was."

I laughed. "God. According to what I heard, everybody in the whole damn department knew about Joan and Bingham."

"I'm sure they did," Janice said. "Academic departments being what they are. But you have to admit it's not the kind of thing they'd want to broadcast to the press. Jesus. Can you picture the headlines? I can see it now in twenty-four point type—'Harvard Prof Shares Love Nest with Coed.' God."

"Yes," I said. "Or maybe, 'Psych Prof Held Midnite Sex Seminars with Murder Victim.'"

Janice laughed.

"It's amazing that you weren't even able to find out about Bingham being Joan's academic adviser," I said. "They really did a great job of deflecting you, didn't they?"

"Stonewalling, it's called," Janice said. "How'd *you* find out about Bingham?"

I glanced at her. She was looking at me very insistently. I shook my head. "Sorry. I can't tell you that."

She continued to look at me for another few seconds and then grinned, reluctantly. "Okay. You're entitled to protect your sources, I guess."

"Gee, thanks," I replied drily.

"This is very hot stuff, though," Janice said. "I don't know how long I can keep a lid on it. The paper comes out tomorrow."

"When's your deadline?" I asked.

She told me.

"Okay," I said. "It'll probably be public knowledge by then, anyway."

"Well, the cops'll almost have to bring Bingham in for questioning, won't they?"

"I can't imagine they wouldn't," I said. "I don't think they pressed him too hard after Joan died, because there wasn't any real evidence to connect him with what happened to her. But now . . ."

"They'll be wanting to speak with him," Janice agreed. "Definitely."

"Mmmm," I said. I thought for a moment. "At the press conference, Jan, did the chief say anything about whether the two murders were connected? Specifics, I mean?"

"Well, he was sort of noncommittal," Janice said. "All anybody could get out of him were that there were some similarities. But hell, we both know what *that* means."

I nodded. I wasn't going to say a word about what Jack had told me earlier. I'd already betrayed enough confidences for one day. Although he'd never actually told me not to say anything to anyone. Probably he just assumed I had the sense to keep my mouth shut.

"Are you thinking," Janice said slowly, "that there was some sort of relationship between Sandra Dembkoski and Bingham like the one between Bingham and Joan?"

I smiled. "How delicately you put it. Maybe I have a dirty mind, but yes, the possibility *did* occur to me."

"Tell you what," Janice said. "How about we go over to William James Hall and do a little investigating?"

"To where?"

"William James Hall," she repeated. "It's where the psych department is. We can hang around, maybe find someone who'll talk to us."

I shrugged. "Sure. Why not?"

20

WILLIAM JAMES HALL was on the corner of Divinity and Kirkland streets, across from the Busch-Reisinger Museum, about two blocks northeast of Harvard Square. Janice and I took the subway from Central to Harvard, crossed Mass. Avenue to Quincy Street, and walked a long block past the faculty club and the Fogg Art Museum. Quincy fed into the intersection of Kirkland and Divinity.

The snow was still coming down like hell, driven by periodic blasts of arctic wind. Quincy Street, like the streets running into Central Square, was virtually free of vehicular and pedestrian traffic. In the storm, Harvard Yard had an almost Dickensian look. I wouldn't have been surprised to see a horse-drawn sleigh glide by.

We came to the corner of Kirkland and Quincy. Across the street an enormous I. M. Pei-ish monolith of white stone and glass reared up out of the earth.

"That's it?" I asked.

"Uh-huh," Janice said.

"Looks like headquarters for the Chemical Bank or something," I observed.

"Oh, sure," Janice replied. "Only difference is, this place probably has more dough to throw around than the Chemical Bank."

"Probably," I said.

We crossed the street and came to a sort of concrete plaza with marble benches. The entrance to William James Hall was a row of glass doors. On one of them someone had taped a handlettered cardboard sign that read NONFUNCTIONAL.

"Oh, Christ," I said, pointing to it. "Will you look at that? Jesus. They could've said the door was broken. But noooooooooooooo." I drew out the word the way John Belushi always had. "They *had* to say the damn thing was nonfunctional."

"Maybe they're trying to be funny," Janice suggested, pushing open one of the functional doors.

"Janice," I sighed, "how many psychologists do you know with a sense of humor?"

"Not a hell of a lot," she admitted.

We found ourselves in a lobby facing a bank of elevators. Welcoming. Over the elevators, in raised gold letters, was a quote from William James. I read it. "The community stagnates without the impulse of the individual. The impulse dies away without the sympathy of the community." I nodded to myself; James had always managed to zero in on the important stuff. If he'd been writing today, he'd probably have said something like, "The dynamic of the community is subject to disruption when deprived of the input of the individual. Failure of the peer group to respond with feedback of a supportive nature will impose negative parameters on individual creative development."

"Gee," I said. "I wonder if the elevators are functional."

"Doesn't take much effort to find out," Janice replied. She went over to the control panel and punched the up button. The doors of one of the elevators slid open almost immediately and we stepped into the car. The doors slid shut behind us.

"So far, so functional," Janice said.

"Yeah," I said. "But where are we going?"

"I've been here before," she said. "I know the floor." She pressed one of the buttons on the elevator control panel, and with a little lurch we started upward.

The elevator disgorged us into a corridor done in beige-flecked linoleum and tan paint. Like most modern office buildings, it had all the warmth and quaint individuality of an aircraft boarding ramp. If you hadn't known you were in an academic department, you'd have assumed you were in the right place to pay your utilities bill or apply for a car loan. I wondered what William James would have thought. Maybe he'd have been pragmatic enough to take it on the chin.

Janice strode off down the corridor, looking as if she knew exactly where she was going. I followed. We went into an office where a gray-haired woman sat typing at a metal desk. A much younger, very slim and pretty dark-haired woman in jeans was shoving folders into a filing cabinet.

The gray-haired woman looked up with a smile and said, "May I help you?"

Janice smiled back at her. "We're looking for Professor Bingham. Could you tell us if he's around this afternoon?"

The woman's face altered subtly. "I believe," she said, "that Professor Bingham is out. He had to go to a meeting at the last minute."

112

"Oh, I see," Janice said. "Do you know when he'll be back?"

The woman eyed us. "Are you graduate students of his?" she asked.

"Yes," Janice said blandly.

The woman consulted a schedule on her desk. "Professor Bingham's office hours are from ten to eleven on Mondays and three to five on Tuesdays. Would you like to make an appointment for one of those times?"

"Oh, gosh," Janice said. "It's kind of an emergency. You see we have this group project on the etiology of coprophilia that's due next week, and we have kind of a problem with one of . . ."

I did my best to look like a supplicant. Had I ever put any of my own students through this kind of crap? God, I hoped not.

The woman was shaking her head. "I'm sorry. Professor Bingham will be busy for the rest of the afternoon. You'll have to make an appointment for sometime next week."

"Oh, but that'll be too late," Janice whined. "The paper's due Monday."

I bit the inside of my lower lip to keep from laughing.

"There's really nothing I can do," the gray-haired woman said.

"Are you sure?" Janice asked. She sounded as if she were on the verge of bursting into tears.

"Sorry," the woman said. She didn't look as if she were overwhelmed with regret.

"Oh, okay," Janice replied sadly. "God, I don't know what I'm going to do."

"Would you like to leave a message?" the gray-haired woman asked, evidently softening in the face of such abject misery.

Janice shook her head. "No, I guess I'll just have to—God, I don't know *what* I'll do."

The woman looked at us without saying anything. She probably went through a similar routine on an average of fourteen times a day. Janice sighed and said to me, "Come on, Liz." We left the office, Janice drooping with dejection. Apparently she was going to play the role of desperate graduate student to the hilt.

When we were far enough from the office not to be overheard, I started to snicker. "You missed your calling," I said. "The stage needs you. *Coprophilia?* God."

"You thought that act was good?" Janice said. She shook her head. "You should have seen me the time I played an attendant at the Scandinavian Institute for Taoist Massage and Holistic Love in Kendall Square."

I let out a hoot. "Sorry I missed it," I said, wiping tears of laughter from my cheeks.

"I wonder what emergency meeting Professor Bingham got called out to this afternoon," Janice asked.

"I don't know," I said. "But I have the distinct feeling he's been called in as special consultant to the Cambridge Police Department in the Stanley–Dembkoski case."

"Yeah, me too," Janice said. "My, my. Sex and scandal in the good old Harvard psych department."

"Hey," a voice behind us said. We looked up in surprise.

The young woman in jeans who'd been feeding the filing cabinet in the secretary's office was standing about ten feet away, her arms folded and a knowing look on her face.

"Oh, hi," Janice said.

The woman came toward us. "What's the deal?" she said.

"Excuse me?" Janice said.

The woman gave a little snorting laugh. "Come off it. You two aren't graduate students here. I know all the graduate students."

There was a little silence. The three of us looked at each other. I raised my eyebrows at Janice. She shrugged slightly.

"Look," the young woman said. "An hour and a half ago two cops showed up here and took Bingham away with them. Now you two show up, pretending to be graduate students, pretending you have to see Bingham right away because of some nonexistent project that's due next week. Like I said, what's the deal?"

Janice sighed. "No deal. We're reporters. We just wanted to talk to him."

"Uh-huh," the woman said. "About what?"

Janice straightened up and gave her a steady look. "Two things."

"Yeah? What are they?"

"Joan Stanley and Sandra Dembkoski," Janice said.

"Oh," the girl said. "I see." There was a peculiar expression on her face. "Yeah. I should have guessed, shouldn't I?"

Janice threw me a lightning glance. Then she looked back at the young woman. "Can we talk to *you* about it?"

The young woman stared at us for a few seconds. Then she shrugged, a gesture that combined disgust and resignation. "Sure. Why the hell not?"

"Where?" I said. It was my first contribution to the conversation.

The girl jerked her head to the right. "In here." She turned, and we followed her into an empty office. Janice sat down in the chair behind the desk. I perched on the windowsill. The woman shut the door and leaned against it, gazing at us warily.

"What's your name?" Janice asked, in a friendly, chatty voice.

"Elaine Diminico," she replied.

"Nice to meet you," Janice said. "I'm Janice Miller. That"—she nodded at me—"is Liz Connors."

"What paper do you work for?"

"I'm free-lance," I said. "Janice works for the *Chronicle.*"

"Big-time," Elaine said.

"We all have to start somewhere," Janice said calmly. "You were expecting maybe Woodward and Bernstein?"

Elaine Diminico shook her head. "No," she said. "Sorry, I didn't mean to sound snotty."

"It's okay," I said, although I was a little annoyed. Hell, no one was forcing Diminico to talk to us.

Janice leaned back in her chair. "Elaine," she said. "How do you know Bingham? Are you a student here? Did you take a course from him?"

Elaine grimaced. "Yes, I am a student here, and yes, I did take a course from Bingham. The asshole."

I kept my face carefully neutral. Janice folded her hands in her lap. "Asshole?" she repeated.

"Also known as Professor Letch," Elaine said. Still with her back pressed to the door, she slid downward until she was sitting on the floor. Her head was down and we couldn't see her face. Janice and I looked at each other.

"Professor Letch," I said. I felt as if I were in an echo chamber. "What does that mean?"

Elaine glanced up at me. She looked as if she had a pain somewhere. "What the hell do you think it means?" She leaned forward and pressed her forehead against her knee.

"Tell us what happened," Janice suggested softly.

Elaine raised her head. Her eyes were wet. "I can't," she murmured. "I can't."

Janice sucked in a sharp breath. I slid off the windowsill and went over to Elaine and knelt down beside her. "That bad?" I said.

She made a gulping noise and started to sob. I bit my lip and closed my eyes.

"Would you like to go somewhere else?" Janice said. "Maybe get some coffee or a drink?"

Elaine shook her head vigorously. Feeling terribly awkward and uncomfortable, I put my hand on her shoulder.

She cried for maybe five minutes, in great tearing sobs that shook her whole body. I patted her shoulder. At the end of it, Janice took a wad of

Kleenex from her purse and silently offered it to Elaine. She took it and wiped her eyes and blew her nose. Then she hiccuped.

"Would you like us to leave you alone now?" I said. Janice shot me an irritated, disgusted look and I glared back at her.

Elaine shook her head. "No. It's okay. I didn't mean to do that."

"Don't apologize," I said. I got up and leaned against the desk. "Do you want to talk about it?"

She nodded.

"What happened?"

She took a deep breath, making a visible effort to collect herself. "I took a course from him last year. In perception."

"Yes?" I said.

She shrugged. "Well, you know. A couple of weeks after the course started, he stopped me after class one day and asked me if I'd have coffee with him." She made a slight face. "He *said* he wanted to discuss some point I'd brought up in class."

"And?"

"Well, it was okay, you know? We went to the Coffee Connection, and he bought me a piece of cheesecake. It was nice. He told me he thought I had an interesting perspective on the subject."

"Uh-huh," I said. "What happened after that?"

"We just started getting together after class. To talk and all."

"And?"

She made a gesture with her hand as if she were chasing away a gnat. "This is hard."

I waited. Janice was watching us as if we were actors playing out the last scene of *Hamlet.*

"I went to his office one afternoon," Elaine said. "And we were just sitting and talking and all of a sudden he got up from behind his desk and came over and grabbed me and kissed me."

Janice snorted. I gave her a warning look.

"Then what?" I said.

"Well, he, you know . . ."

"Let me guess," I said. "He told you how intelligent you were and how he'd never met a student with such a flair for the subject, and how sensitive—"

"How did you know?" Elaine interrupted, looking up at me in surprise.

I laughed, although I wasn't particularly amused. "Honey, it's a line as old as Socrates."

116

"Oh," Elaine said. She looked faintly startled.

"So you had an affair with him," I said bluntly.

She nodded mutely.

"How long did it last?"

"Oh, I guess maybe two months." She gave a long, shuddering sigh. "Then he just dumped me. Boom. Like that. I mean, it was so *weird*. One day we were together and the next he wouldn't even talk to me."

I looked at Janice. She closed her eyes and shook her head slowly, wearily. I looked back at Elaine Diminico. She was staring fixedly at the wall opposite, her face stiff with pain.

"Elaine," I said. "I don't know what kind of consolation this will be; probably none whatsoever. But"—I paused and took a deep breath— "we've all had a Bingham in our lives."

She gave me a faint smile.

"You'll be okay," I said. "What happened next?"

"Nothing. The course ended. I got a B minus."

"A B minus," Janice said. "Christ."

"Yeah," Elaine said. "He really ripped up my final paper. Said it didn't have the proper documentation."

"What could you expect?" I said. "From someone like that?"

"I suppose," Elaine said. "God! How could I have been such a jerk?"

"It wasn't your fault," I said. "We're all jerks in situations like that."

"Elaine," Janice said, "did Bingham do the same thing to Sandra Dembkoski and Joan Stanley that he did to you?"

Elaine looked uncomfortable.

"It's okay," I said. "You can tell us."

Elaine sighed. "He started up with Joan about a month after he dumped me."

"Did you ever talk to her about it?" I asked.

Elaine shook her head. "No. I figured there wasn't any point. She'd just think I was jealous or something."

"That's usually the way it works," I agreed. "What about with Sandra?"

Elaine's face was pensive. "Well, there was a rumor going around—this was before I got into it with Chris—that he was screwing around with one of the secretaries."

"Whooo," Janice exclaimed softly.

"It had to have been Sandy," Elaine continued. "It sure as hell wasn't Mrs. Farnham."

"Mrs. Farnham?" I queried.

"The old bitch in the office," Elaine explained. "She's been here about five million years. The one who told you you had to make an appointment with his lordship a month in advance or something."

"What happened with Bingham and Sandy?" I asked.

Elaine snorted. "Nothing. He fucked her once or twice and then dumped her, was what I heard."

"Not sufficiently intellectual for him, I guess," Janice remarked.

"Yeah," Elaine said. All of a sudden, she looked ready to cry again.

"Elaine," I said gently. "Did you love Bingham?"

She nodded, her head down. She was making little whimpering noises, like a puppy that's been left alone in the dark too long.

"Elaine," I said. "This is important. Did Bingham ever hurt you? Physically, I mean?"

She shook her head, sniffling. I straightened up slowly, feeling cramped and old, and glanced at Janice. She nodded very slightly. I bent down again and touched Elaine on the shoulder.

"I think maybe you'd like to be alone now," I said.

She nodded. "Thanks." She slid over sideways so that she was no longer sitting with her back pressed against the door.

"It was nice of you to talk to us," Janice said quietly.

"Yeah," Elaine said. "You're welcome."

Riding down in the elevator, neither Janice nor I said anything. Maybe there wasn't anything to say. Janice looked extremely thoughtful and a little sad. I must have had a similar expression on my own face.

The lobby was deserted. As we walked across it, our footsteps echoed hollowly on the green flagstone floor. The sound was an eerie and sort of lonely one.

Outside it had gotten quite dark. The snow was still blowing around in a white fury. We crossed the plaza and stopped at the corner of Kirkland. Traffic crept along down the street.

"Are you as depressed as I am?" Janice asked abruptly.

I expelled a long sigh. "Maybe more," I said.

118

21

IT WASN'T UNTIL we were on the subway and heading back toward Central Square that either one of us spoke again.

"Beyond being depressed," Janice said. "What do you think?"

I shrugged. "I don't know. Some parts fit; others don't. Bingham sounds like a real slimy character, but does that make him a murderer?"

"Not necessarily," Janice said. "But, look. Stanley and Dembkoski were probably killed by the same guy. And I can't believe it was somebody who was a total stranger to either one of them. Both of them were fooling around with Bingham, and not terribly happily, either, by the sound of it. Doesn't that at least suggest something to you?"

"Sure," I said. "But it proves nothing. We don't know what other acquaintances Joan and Sandy had in common. That William James Hall is a big place. They could have been friendly with a lot of the same people."

"Uh-huh," Janice said. "And out of that whole bunch, Sandy and Joan just happened to go to bed only with the same guys. Bingham and somebody else? Who also killed them?"

"Why not?" I said. "More bizarre things have happened. Listen, I'm not saying Bingham is a blessed innocent. Maybe he *did* kill the two of them. But then again, maybe he didn't. Maybe the fact that Joan and Sandy worked in the same place and knew the same people and went to bed with the same guy has nothing to do with them getting killed. You said so yourself—it could just be an incredible coincidence. Maybe everything is a coincidence. Why are we arguing about this? If Bingham has an alibi for last night, and there isn't any kind of physical evidence to connect him with Stanley or Dembkoski, then he's out of the running, right? We'll find out soon enough."

The train rumbled into Central Square station and stopped with a swaying lurch. Janice and I fought our way out of the crowded car and onto the platform. I wrinkled my nose; it had the overpoweringly urinous smell that all subway stations do in wet weather. An ancient wizened little toothless man in an army surplus trenchcoat bearing a rich variety of new and old stains staggered up to us and asked Janice for a quarter.

"Why?" she asked.

"Because I'm a coin collector," he replied.

We gave him fifty cents and he told us that surely the Lord Jesus would bless us. Then he tottered off to hit up a kid in a Tufts jacket who'd gotten off the train behind us.

"I wonder how much he takes in with that routine?" Janice asked.

"Probably about seventy-five bucks a day," I said.

She made a squawking noise. "That's about a third of what I get each week. Before taxes."

"Obviously," I said, "you're in the wrong racket."

"Tell me about it," she said. We went up the stairs to the street.

The plows were out in full force and had cleared some of the mess from the streets. The snowbanks they'd pushed up on the sidewalks would be here until next April, of course, getting bigger and dirtier as the winter progressed. I wondered if you were to cut through one in the spring you'd find rings of age, the way you do in the trunk of a tree.

There were two new trucks outside the police station, one from Channel Four and the other from Channel Five.

"Oooh," Janice said. "*Something* must be doing."

We went through the double doors of the main entrance to the station and walked right into a klieg-lit circus. There were maybe fifty people milling around the desk area, most of them belonging to the technical crews that hovered around the T.V. reporters like pilot fish. I spotted Sheila McAndrew, the woman from Channel Five, over by the desk.

A uniformed cop I didn't know stopped us as we were coming through the doors and asked us if we needed any help. It was a polite way of finding out what the hell we were doing in the station. The question actually surprised me a bit. Ordinarily the Cambridge police didn't seem to care who wandered into their house as long as you didn't do so toting a bazooka or something at high port. They didn't even make you sign in or wear a visitor's pass. Then it occurred to me that the cops, accustomed as they were to a steady stream of drop-in drunks and waifs and groupies and people who had conclusive proof that M.I.T. was a wholly owned subsidiary of the K.G.B., were probably getting sick of tripping over television cables and being chased down corridors by people brandishing tape recorders and hand mikes. I couldn't blame them.

"We're press," Janice announced.

The cop rolled his eyes at the ceiling. "Hey, what a bonus," he said. "Just what we need more of right now."

"What can I tell you?" Janice said. "It's my job."

"Yeah," the cop said. "That's what they all say. All right, girls, you can come on in. Two more won't make no difference, I guess." He walked away, shaking his head slowly.

"I have received more enthusiastic welcomes in my time," I said.

"Me, too," Janice replied. "Well, it goes with the territory. If you're going to be a professional pain in the ass, you have to expect people won't be all that thrilled to see you all the time, right? Oh, well. I can live with it."

"Don't have much choice, do you?" I asked.

She laughed. "No."

There was a sudden flurry of movement at the other end of the room. Automatically Janice and I looked over in that direction. The reporters were converging as a group at the foot of the stairs leading to the second floor. Sheila McAndrew, I noticed, was in the forefront. Aggressive.

Something was obviously about to happen. Lemminglike, Janice and I moved closer to the group.

Jack and Sam Flaherty, the red-headed detective-sergeant I'd last seen the day of Joan Stanley's funeral, were coming down the stairs. Between them was a man in an investment banker's gray pin-striped suit. He and the others halted when they saw what was waiting for them at the foot of the stairs. The man's right hand went reflexively to his collar and made a minute adjustment to the knot of his tie. I wondered if next he'd pat his hair into place and pinch his cheeks to give them color. I glanced at Jack. He was leaning against the banister, looking impassive. I knew that lack of expression as a mask for boredom and impatience.

The man in the gray suit took another step down the stairs and paused again.

"Betcha that's Bingham," Janice hissed at me.

I didn't reply. I was too busy staring at the man, inventorying his looks.

Psych professors, in my experience anyway, tend not to be a terribly physically prepossessing lot. Around Cambridge, you can spot them a mile off. They're the guys with the green canvas backpacks for toting books and lecture notes, the shapeless chinos, and the twenty-five-year-old tweed jackets that look as if they've been used as a dog's bed. And, of course, the obligatory scraggly beard and a pipe that smells like Secaucus.

Bingham was something different.

He may have been an s.o.b., but he was a *good-looking* s.o.b. He was perhaps six-two and rapier-slim and elegant. He had thick tawny hair styled in a helmet of curls, and a long firm-jawed face. His mouth was wide and well cut. Behind a pair of gold-rimmed aviator glasses, his eyes moved over the group of reporters, not nervously but coolly, assessingly. He had an air about him, not of anything so crass as superiority, but a kind of amused arrogance. The Olympian among plebes.

"Well, there he is," Janice said. "The heartbreak kid. The superstud of William James Hall."

I started to laugh and then caught myself. One of the reporters was asking the man a question.

"Professor Bingham, we understand you're here in connection with the murders of Joan Stanley and Sandra Dembkoski. Could you tell us, please, what your involvement in the case is?"

Bingham smiled. "I'd be happy to. The fact of the matter is, I've been asked by the police to draw up a psychiatric profile of the killer to assist them in their investigation. Naturally, I'm glad to be of whatever help I can."

I glanced quickly at Jack. For about a quarter of a second, he looked as if he'd just bitten into a piece of rancid meat. Then his face smoothed back into its impassive mask.

"Can you describe to us, Professor, what kind of individual the killer might be?" Sheila McAndrew called. "In layman's terms," she added. Some of the other reporters laughed.

Bingham laughed with them. "That may be difficult," he said. "But—to use, as you say, layman's terms, I would describe this man as quite possibly a rather rigid, repressed personality, colorless if you will."

"But obviously one with a special hatred for women," Sheila McAndrew interjected.

Bingham looked faintly annoyed at the interruption. "Yes, certainly," he said. "But this would not be apparent under day-to-day circumstances. This would be a person who would live quietly, calling no special attention to himself by his habits or routines."

"A loner," Sheila McAndrew said quickly.

"Almost assuredly," Bingham replied.

"What might his personal characteristics be?" McAndrew shot back.

Bingham looked thoughtful. "This type of individual would be very likely to be neat and orderly in his personal habits, and extremely polite and punctual. Correct. Capable, possibly, of seeming to be gentle and compassionate. Unremarkable in terms of physical appearance. Perhaps the best word to describe him would be *unassuming*."

"But a killer," a man from the *Herald* said.

"Yes, indeed," Bingham replied. "A killer."

"Why?" Sheila McAndrew asked. She seemed determined to regain and hold on to centerstage. "How would such a person be capable of committing such brutal acts?"

"For that," Bingham said, "we would have to look to his past. Such an individual would very likely have been the product of a largely female-dominated home environment."

"Of course, what else," Janice murmured sardonically. One of the cops standing nearby overheard her and snickered.

"Very possibly, the father would have died or abandoned the family during the killer's infancy or early childhood," Bingham continued imperturbably. "He would therefore have been raised by his mother, a person who might be described as superficially passive but in actual fact domineering. Capricious in her affections toward the child. Like the killer himself, she would probably be compulsively neat, orderly, and punctual. Excessively concerned with personal cleanliness." Bingham paused, eyed the reporters calmly, and added, "A woman who would make sexual overtures toward her son."

The final remark elicited, as it was intended to do, a muted outcry from the group. Bingham smiled, clearly amused and gratified by the effect of his words.

"Could you explain your comment, sir?" Sheila McAndrew's voice soared above those of the other reporters.

"Of course," Bingham replied. "The mother would be the type of person who might permit her son to watch her bathe. Or she might undress in front of him. Yet she would respond with violent rage and swift punishment to any normal sexual reaction on his part."

"So he'd grow up hating all women because of that?" Sheila McAndrew asked. She sounded a little dubious.

"He would grow up suffering from severe heterosexual inhibitions," Bingham replied. "He would seek to have intercourse with women, but be capable of doing so only if able to fantasize situations in which he raped or tortured those women."

"Charming," Janice muttered, and made a face.

"In sum," Bingham said, "I would suggest to the police that they look for a man very likely no younger than thirty, quite possibly considerably older, reasonably intelligent but not necessarily well-educated, and probably of a lower socioeconomic background. In him, I think, they would find their murderer."

"That narrows it down a lot," I whispered to Janice. "To three quarters of the adult male population of East Cambridge, to be exact."

At that moment, Jack leaned forward and said a few words to Bingham.

Bingham looked somewhat surprised and, following that, irritated. He murmured something to Jack. Jack shrugged and shook his head. Bingham opened his mouth as if to say something further to Jack, apparently thought better of it, and turned back to the assembled reporters.

"Professor," a man from the *Globe* yelled, "Professor, could you tell us, please—"

Bingham held up his right hand. "I'm sorry," he said, with a rueful smile. "No more questions. I've just been advised by the lieutenant that I have not only the right but the *duty* to remain silent at this juncture."

The crowd laughed.

You arrogant, snide twerp, I thought.

Bingham came down the remaining steps and maneuvered his way through the group of reporters. Someone shouted something at him and shoved a mike into his face. He smiled again and shook his head. "The appropriate phrase, I believe, is *no comment*," he said.

I seriously considered tripping him as he walked by me. But I couldn't get close enough to the son of a bitch. Probably just as well.

I turned, instead, to speak to Janice, but she was gone. Puzzled, I glanced around the room. I spotted her standing in line waiting to use the pay phone. I walked over to her.

"What do you think?" I said.

"About Bingham?" She shrugged. "Obviously, he's not under arrest for murder, is he?"

"Apparently not."

"Too bad," she said. "Pompous prick."

I burst out laughing. "I think you and I were predisposed not to like him. But I had the feeling the other reporters thought he was pretty impressive. Except maybe for Sheila."

"She has some brains," Janice admitted grudgingly. "For a talking hairdo."

"What are you going to do now?" I asked.

"Make a phone call," she said. "And write my story. What else?"

I nodded. "Yeah. I suppose I ought to take off, too."

"You don't have a deadline," Janice said.

"No," I conceded. "But I have notes to organize."

"I guess," she said. She glanced around, as if to make sure no one was eavesdropping, and added softly. "Thanks for the tip. About Bingham and Joan, I mean."

"You can't put *that* in your story," I said, aghast. "He'd sue."

"Doesn't matter," she replied. "It's good to know anyway. Even if I can't print it."

"Well, you're welcome," I said. "Good luck with the story."

"Thanks; you too. Keep in touch, huh? Especially if you hear about any more late-breaking Harvard sex scandals."

I grinned. "Sure. Talk to you later."

"Uh-huh."

I left her to wait for the phone to free up and wandered, with what I thought was a good simulation of aimlessness, across the room to the foot of the stairs. Just as I'd done earlier this afternoon, I loitered there until I was fairly sure no one was looking in my direction. Then I bounded up the steps.

Sometimes I think I should work for the C.I.A. Covert operations are my specialty.

The door to Jack's office was open. I knocked on the jamb.

"Come on in," he called. I walked into the office. Jack was sitting behind his desk, scribbling something on a yellow lined pad. At the sound of my footsteps he looked up and smiled.

"Somehow I thought you'd turn up here again," he said. He put down his pen and leaned back in the chair. "Were you at that circus downstairs a few minutes ago?"

I nodded and sat down in the chair across from the desk. "How do you do it?"

He looked puzzled. "Do what?"

"Hang on to your temper. If that had been me down there on the steps with Bingham, I'd have kicked him in the balls or something when he made that crack about you telling him to shut up."

Jack smiled. "How long do you think I'd've lasted in this job if I went around kicking everyone in the balls who annoyed me?"

I considered that. "True," I said finally. I shook my head. "He *is* an incredible turkey, though, isn't he?"

"Uh-huh."

"Did you *really* ask him to help you?" I asked. I found the notion unbelievable.

"No," Jack replied. "I didn't. He offered."

"And you accepted?"

Jack shrugged. "I want him cooperative. That was a good way to ensure it."

"Oh." I undid the snaps on my windbreaker. "So why'd you tell him to stuff a sock in it? Was he about to spill something you want kept secret?"

125

"Oh, hell, no," Jack said. "I just got sick of the sound of his voice."

I wriggled out of my windbreaker and draped it over the back of the chair. "I take it you don't think Bingham killed either Joan or Sandra, huh?"

"No."

"May I ask why not?"

"Sure." He gave me another smile.

"Well?"

"For one thing, Bingham was in New York last night. Giving an address at the, uh—" He broke off and glanced down at a paper on his desk. "At the American Society of Clinical Psychologists' annual convention. In the Versailles Room at the Carlyle, from six to seven. After that, he was at dinner with eight other people, and after that, at another meeting that didn't break up until two A.M. He didn't get back to Boston until nine-thirty this morning."

"He could prove all that?" I said suspiciously.

"I checked it, dear," Jack said.

"Of course," I said. "Silly me. What about Joan? Any connection with Bingham there? I mean other than the one that he was fooling around with her?"

"His blood type's O."

I nodded. "So much for Bingham as a suspect."

"So much for Bingham," Jack agreed.

"You never thought he was a serious contender anyway, did you?" I asked.

"No."

"Why not?"

He shrugged. "To me, he didn't feel right for it."

I sighed. "Well, your feelings, or whatever they are, have been exactly on target so far. You didn't think Andy MacKenzie was it, and he wasn't, and you didn't think Richie Kearns was it for Joan, and he almost certainly wasn't, and now you've eliminated Bingham. So . . . who killed Joan and/or Sandra?"

He was silent, looking at me.

"You have *no* thoughts on the subject?"

"I don't even know for sure if I'm looking for one guy or two."

I laughed shortly. "Bingham seems confident it's one guy."

"Yeah, well, that's his privilege."

"But you told me before you were pretty sure it was one guy. That killed Joan and Sandra."

"Well, that's what I think on the basis of what I saw today. Maybe the lab tests will confirm it. My guess is, they will. But they won't tell me the guy's name or where I can find him."

"I know," I said. "I know. God, what a mess."

"Uh-huh."

"I wish I could think of some way to help you."

He smiled slightly. "Thank you."

"I'm not just saying that. I *mean* it."

"I believe you."

We sat looking at each other for a few moments. Then I leaned over and reached my hand across the desk. He took it and squeezed it. His hand felt warm and strong.

"So," I said presently. "What did you think of Professor Bingham's psychiatric profile?"

Jack let go of my hand and lifted his right shoulder in a semishrug.

"Does that mean you don't buy it?"

"Not necessarily. It could be letter-perfect. On the other hand . . ." His voice trailed off.

"On the other hand what?"

"It could also be a crock of shit."

I nodded. "How useful are those things in general? Profiles, I mean."

"It depends. Sometimes they help, a little. Mostly what's useful in them is common sense, though, stuff anybody with any experience with criminals could figure out. The rest is too vague to be much good." He leaned forward in his chair, gesturing a little with his right hand. "I mean, how much point is there in a shrink telling me that a guy who kills and rapes women is hostile toward women? Christ, I can deduce that much for myself."

I nodded. "And there's something else wrong, too."

Jack raised his eyebrows. "Which is?"

"The way Bingham described the killer. As some kind of—well, as a Caspar Milquetoast type, basically."

"Yeah?"

"Does that sound like the kind of a guy a young woman like either Joan or Sandra would find attractive?"

"How would I know?"

"Oh, Jack. You know what I mean. A prissy, neat, fussy old maid type of man? When they had the option of getting it on with someone as gorgeous as Bingham?"

"Wait a minute," Jack interrupted. He was looking at me very hard. "They? Bingham?"

I blinked in surprise. "Sure. Sandra was fooling around with him too. Didn't you know that?" I stopped and stared at Jack, confused. "You must have. I figured that was one of the reasons you dragged him here today."

"Yeah, that was a contributing factor," Jack replied drily. "What I'm wondering is, how did *you* find out about him and Sandra?"

I told him about the conversation Janice Miller and I had had with Elaine Diminico.

"I see," Jack said, when I'd finished. "So what's your point?"

"Before I get to that," I said. "You tell *me* something."

"Okay." He sounded amused.

"Your going assumption is that whoever killed Sandra and Joan was not only the same person, but someone they knew, right? Someone they were expecting to see on the nights they got killed."

"That's my best guess."

"Right. Now." I got up and started pacing around the room, my usual habit when I'm trying to figure something out. "Let's put aside Joan for the moment and concentrate on Sandra. Okay, granted she slept around. But still, she must have had *some* standards." I smiled at Jack. "She seemed to think you were pretty nice, after all."

"Yeah, she showed good taste there," he agreed.

"Yes. Well, we'll pursue that topic later. The thing is, Jack, would she have gone for the Mr. Peepers type Bingham was speculating about? When she had a town full of horny twenty-two-year old Harvard and Tufts and M.I.T. jocks *and* adorable detective-lieutenants to choose from?"

"Is there such a thing as an M.I.T. jock?" Jack smiled.

"Okay, a handsome young stud of an M.I.T. chemical engineer," I said. "Contradiction in terms though that may be, too. But don't let's split hairs. You know what I'm saying." I collapsed back into my chair. "God! If you were a twenty-one-year-old swinger and *you* had a choice between Tom Selleck and Wally Cox, who would *you* take to bed?"

"Gee," Jack said. "Do I have to choose either? Couldn't you fix me up with Clint Eastwood? I think he's more my type."

I looked at him blankly for a second and then laughed. "I'll see what I can do, sweetie."

"Oh, hey, you will? Thanks."

"Seriously," I said. "Does what I'm saying about Sandra make sense? I can see, now, what she and Joan saw in Bingham. True, he's a dork. But he does have a certain amount of power and prestige, in addition to his looks, and those things do have an aphrodisiac effect on some women. Especially young ones. But . . . the guy in Bingham's profile is a *wimp*. A *wimp*. Would a girl like Sandra even look at someone like that? Much less bother to invite him to her apartment and to her bed?"

Jack was quiet for a few seconds after I'd wound up my diatribe. Then he said, "Want a job?"

"Say what?"

He smiled. "I'd like to hire you as an investigator."

My mouth fell open. "Are you serious?"

"Well, I can hardly issue you a badge or a gun. But you would probably be goddamned good at this kind of work."

Bemused, I shook my head. "That's the nicest thing you've ever said to me."

He looked taken aback. "Oh, come now. Surely not the *nicest*."

I smiled. "Well, the second nicest. Wow. So you think that maybe I'm right about Sandra and Joan?"

"It makes sense," he said. "It makes a lot of sense. Yeah. You could be right. I think you probably are."

"So do I." I leaned back in my chair and put one foot up on the edge of his desk and grinned, feeling terribly impressed with myself. Liz Connors, girl detective. Slickest operator in the East. The secrets of no soul hidden from me.

"*Damn*," I said. I let my foot slide off the edge of the desk and fall to the floor with a thud.

"What's the matter?" Jack asked, sounding concerned.

I sighed. "While I was sitting here reflecting on what a stupendous intellect I am, it occurred to me that my little speculations don't really put you any further ahead in the game than Bingham's profile did."

"Oh?"

I curled my lip. "Well, what questions got answered? Like if Joan and Sandra got killed by the same guy, and it wasn't Bingham, was it just a coincidence? Or was there some connection between them?"

"That," Jack said. "Is one of the things I intend to try and find out."

"But how?"

He smiled. "I'll think of a way."

22

HE DID. THURSDAY afternoon he called me at my apartment and asked me for a date. It was the first time he'd done that in longer than I could remember. When you've been with someone exclusively for a year and a half, you don't have to make formal arrangements to see each other. You just *do* it, I guess.

Anyway, Thursday afternoon he called to ask me if I'd "go out" with him that evening.

"What did you have in mind?" I asked, amused. "A Frankie Avalon–Annette Funicello movie and a chocolate soda afterward at the malt shop?"

"No. Something a *lot* more exciting than that."

"Oh, because my mommy and my daddy don't let me stay out too late on school nights."

"Hey, you'll be with a cop. What do they have to worry about?"

"Right you are," I said. "Okay, cutie-pie, where is it you're taking me?"

"My dear, I am going to introduce you to all the drama, all the color, all the pageantry of . . ." He broke off with a dramatic pause.

"Yes, yes," I said, in tones of great urgency, playing along with the gag. "Don't keep me in suspense. What is it you're going to introduce me to?"

"The Cambridge singles scene." He gave each individual word the booming ponderous enunciation of the announcer for Monday Night Football calling a particularly spectacular play.

"I beg your pardon?" I said.

"The bars, babe, the bars," Jack replied. "You know—where the young and the restless go in search of a soulmate or maybe just one fleeting night of ecstasy."

"Jesus H. Christ." I said. I held the phone away from my ear and grimaced at it. Then I brought the receiver back up to my face and said, "What the hell did you drink for breakfast? A quart of bourbon?"

He laughed.

"Jack?"

"Yes?"

"Are you serious?"

"Uh-huh."

"Oh, I've never been to one of those places. A singles bar, I mean."

"Then it's high time you had the experience."

I turned that comment over in my mind. I wasn't at all sure I agreed with him, but I didn't feel like debating the point. "Okay, sure. What the hell—maybe it'll be good for a laugh. When will you pick me up?"

"Eight-thirty?"

"Sure. See you then. Jack?"

"Yeah?"

"Is there a point to this escapade? I mean, what you have planned for us doesn't sound like your or my notion of a typical fun evening."

"Oh, yes," he said. "There's a point." He didn't elaborate.

"Well?" I said, after a few seconds of pregnant silence had elapsed.

"You want to help me do some investigating?" he asked.

"Yes, of course," I replied, mystified.

"This is your golden opportunity," he said, and hung up.

I replaced the receiver in the telephone cradle, shaking my head. Then I went to my bedroom closet to check out the contents and see if I had anything appropriate to wear for a night out on the town. I wasn't quite sure what was the correct attire for a thirty-three-year-old woman about to make a first foray into the Cambridge singles scene, as Jack had called it. I was fairly certain my tweed suit bought at the last Brooks Brothers sale or jeans and a fisherman's sweater wouldn't do. Nor would the gray Edwardian-style Laura Ashley dress with the dropped waist that I'd worn when Jack had taken me to the testimonial dinner on behalf of a retiring C.P.D. captain at the Sheraton-Commander.

Ordinarily, clothing is something I give about as much thought to as I spend time pondering the subtler ramifications of the foreign policy of Luxembourg.

After about thirty minutes' worth of concerted rummaging, I ran across something I thought might pass muster even in the most determinedly trendy of Cambridge watering holes. Then I went to mess around with my hair.

Jack arrived at my place at eight-twenty-nine that evening. I opened the apartment door and he looked at me and said, "Holy Christ."

"What's the matter?" I asked, stepping back to give him a better view. "Don't you like it?"

"I love it," he replied. "But is it safe for you to go out in public looking like that?"

I shrugged. "If I'm with a cop, what harm can possibly come to me?"

131

"Don't ask," he replied. He looked at me again and shook his head. "Jesus!"

"Well, don't stand there in the hall," I said. "Come in."

I was wearing an outfit I'd bought on sale and on impulse at T. J. Maxx three months ago and never till now had had the courage to clip the price tags from. It was a princess-cut dark green velvet dress with long sleeves and slightly puffed shoulders. Demurely knee length. Modestly high-backed. It also had virtually no front. The bodice slashed down in a deep V that ended about four inches above my navel.

Jack walked into the room and then around me in a slow circle, staring. He himself was dazzling in a navy blue blazer, gray slacks, white shirt, and red-and-blue diagonally striped tie.

"You look nice," I said.

"Not as nice as you," he replied.

"Well, we're both gorgeous," I said. On my feet I had very high spike-heeled evening sandals, another thing I usually never wore. In them I was only about two inches shy of Jack's six-three. Stepping out together dressed as we were, we'd probably be mistaken by most people for part of the *Vogue* basketball team.

"Want a drink?" I asked.

"No," he said. "We've got enough boozing ahead of us tonight without getting a head start on it here."

I laughed. "I'll get my coat."

"You do that," he said, and reached down to give Lucy a scratch behind the ears.

When we were in the car, I said, "What's the first stop on this magical mystery tour? And what is it exactly that you want me to do? Investigationwise, I mean?"

"The first stop," Jack said, "is that bar on Brattle Street. The one behind the Crate and Barrel. And I don't want you to *do* anything. Just look around and listen and give me your impressions."

"Sure," I said. "But . . . why? What's the purpose?"

He smiled and shook his head. "I'll explain later."

"Okay, the hell with you." I grinned. "Keep your crummy little secrets."

He laughed.

We found a parking place on Concord Avenue and walked the four blocks to the bar on Brattle Street. I had to hang on to Jack's arm all the way. It had stopped snowing last night, and the sidewalks were fairly clear, but I felt terribly wobbly and insecure in my unaccustomedly high heels.

It would probably be wise if I drank only sparingly this evening. Didn't want to trip and fall down and make an ass of myself in public.

The bar we were headed for was attached to a rather chic, expensive restaurant and was called the Cornucopia. I'd been in there a few times with Jack, most recently the night Sandra Dembkoski had tried to pick him up. The place had a sort of schizoid reputation. During the day and early in the evening, it was a perfectly nice, relaxed place to go and have a drink and something to eat. I'd heard that around nine every Thursday, Friday, and Saturday night, though, the place turned into a cross between a Hieronymus Bosch painting and a scene from *Annie Hall*. I'd never seen it in its latter incarnation. I felt like an anthropologist about to begin research on an aboriginal tribe known for its particularly *outré* rites and customs. Good thing I had an armed bodyguard with me.

Jack and I walked into the place on the dot of nine. It was packed to the rafters. Every table was taken, and there were people four deep around the bar. The noise level was unbelievable. There must have been a hundred different conversations all going on at the same time. The air was purple with cigarette and pipe smoke.

We edged into the room and sidled along the wall until we found a small open space by the entrance to the hall leading to the restaurant.

I took a deep breath and peered around me. "My God," I murmured.

There was a burst of loud laughter about three inches from my right ear. I winced.

"Want a drink?" Jack asked.

"Not want," I said. "*Need*."

"Right. Vodka martini?"

"Make it a double."

He laughed and moved away to the bar. I stayed behind to guard our space.

I looked around the room again. The people in it seemed to run remarkably to type. Mostly around my age, I guessed, with a sprinkling of older men. The kind of older man who keeps a briar clenched between his teeth even while speaking and has a distinguished shock of well-groomed white hair and wears turtlenecks and Harris tweed jackets with leather patches on the elbows. The men my age all looked as if they were journalists or assistant professors or lawyers or doctors or novelists or management consultants. The women were a little harder to classify. Some of them belonged to that uniquely Cambridge type that affects long frizzy hair, peasant skirts from Mykonos, yellowing antique blouses from Arsenic and Old Lace, boots from The Tannery, and a molting fur wrap from the Goodwill.

Haute funk, I guess you'd call the style. There were a number of other ladies who looked as if they lived at Bloomingdale's. And a few Sandra Dembkoski clones in skintight satiny-looking slacks and shirts.

Jack reappeared with our drinks. He smiled at me and said, "Aren't you going to take off your coat? It's awfully warm in here."

I glanced down at my front automatically. "I don't know. I feel kind of funny about this dress now," I said. "After what you were saying back at my place."

"That's ridiculous," he replied. "I was only teasing you before. You look terrific. Besides, there's at least ten women in here with more skin showing than you have."

"Oh, you checked that out already, did you?"

He grinned and took a sip of his drink. I handed him my glass, slipped out of my coat, and looked around for a place to put it. There wasn't any, so I draped it over my arm. Jack gave me back my drink.

"Why won't you tell me why it is we're here?" I asked. "Or at the very least, what it is I'm supposed to be looking and listening for?"

"Whatever it is you see or hear that sticks with you," he said. "That's as far as I'll go by way of explanation now. I don't want to influence your, ah, observations."

I raised my eyebrows. "Okay."

We passed the next twenty minutes looking and listening. Actually, there was little else to do but that. The din in the place made it hard to talk privately, since you had to either yell or repeat yourself five times in order to be understood. The crowd was getting denser by the minute; a steady stream of people was coming through the door and virtually no one was leaving. I noticed that most of the new arrivals were either women in pairs or lone men.

I finished up my drink, put my mouth up to Jack's ear, and said, "Excuse me."

He looked surprised. "Where you going?"

"Ladies' room," I replied. "My ears are starting to ring. I need a few seconds of peace and quiet."

"Hope you find it," he said. "I'll be here when you get back."

"You better," I said. I patted him on the shoulder and turned down the narrow hall to the rest rooms.

The ladies' room was minuscule and overwhelmingly redolent of gardenia-scented disinfectant. There was one other woman in there. She was bent forward over the sink, peering intently into the mirror and brushing mascara onto her eyelashes. I leaned against the door of one of the stalls and watched her. She glanced over at me and smiled. She was extraordinarily pretty, with shoulder-length glossy blue-black hair and enormous brown eyes.

"Did you want to use the sink?" she said. "I'll be finished in just a second."

"That's okay," I said, smiling. "Take your time. I'm not in a hurry."

"Oh," she said. She screwed the mascara wand back into its container and dropped it into her purse. "Just came in for a breather, huh?"

"Something like that."

The woman removed a small brown compact from her purse, opened it, and began applying blushing gel to her cheeks. "I know the feeling. It's a nice place, but it can sort of get to you after a while."

I nodded. "It's the noise, mostly. Do you come here a lot?"

The woman laughed. "To the ladies' room?"

I grinned. "No. To this bar."

She shrugged and closed the blusher compact with a little snap. "Oh, off and on, you know? It's a pretty good crowd that comes here. Not like some of those meat racks in Boston. One or two of the guys can be a little . . ." She made a seesawing motion with her right hand. "But you don't really get hassled or anything."

"Oh, that's good," I replied inanely. What else was I supposed to say?

"What about you?" the woman asked.

"Me?"

"Yes. Do *you* come here a lot?"

I laughed. "This is my first time. In fact, I've never even been in a place like this before tonight."

"Oh, wow," the woman said. "No wonder you're hiding out in the ladies' room." Her mouth quirked in a small sympathetic smile.

"Well, I guess I feel a little intimidated," I said. "Or overwhelmed. Or something like that."

The woman took out a lip pencil and began outlining her upper lip. "Yeah, I know. I felt that way at first, too. But"—she shrugged—"you just have to keep telling yourself that it's what you have to do if you want to meet a guy. These days, anyway."

"I guess so," I said.

She nodded and then stepped back to eye her reflection in the mirror. She made a small adjustment to the collar of her shirt. Then she picked up her purse, heaved a theatrical sigh, and said, "Well, time to get back to the trenches."

I wasn't quite sure what the appropriate response was to a remark like that. Good luck? Happy hunting? Don't take any wooden nickels?

"Have fun," I said.

"I'll try," she said, and went out the door. A half-second later she poked her head back into the room, gave me a big grin, and said, "*Courage.*" Then she was gone again.

Courage. Right on, sister.

I combed my hair and washed my hands and reapplied my lipstick. Then I went out to rejoin Jack.

"You were gone a long time," he observed.

"Yes, I know. I struck up a conversation with a woman in there."

Jack nodded. "Like another drink?"

"Sure."

"Okay. Back in a minute." He moved off into the crowd. A couple of women turned to look at him as he went by them.

I glanced around the room again. Almost everyone was in groups of twos and threes and fours, talking a mile a minute and laughing and being as animated as hell. There were a few loners sniffing around the edges of things, trying to insinuate themselves into this or that conversation. The scene had very much the air of a large, crowded cocktail party. But for all their animation, none of the guests appeared to me to be having a very good time. There was something about all the frenetic gaiety that struck me as contrived.

Or was I only reacting to my own feelings of discomfort, imagining an atmosphere of strain because that was precisely what I expected to find in a place like this? For all I knew, everyone here was having the time of his or her life, Maybe *I* was the misfit, the cynical specter at the feast.

"Hello," a voice said at my elbow. Startled, I turned, half expecting to see Jack.

A thin young man a little shorter than I, with curly dark hair and horn-rimmed glasses, was standing about four inches to my left. He had on jeans and blue Nikes and a baggy maroon sweater. There was a sort of happy-go-lucky boyish air of good nature about him. He was smiling at me. Actually he was smiling at the opening in my dress.

"Hi," I said.

"You look sort of lost," he said. "You here by yourself?"

"No," I said, shaking my head and smiling. "My friend's just gone to the bar to get us a drink."

"Oh," he replied. He glanced over his shoulder at the mob around the bar. "Which one is she?"

136

"It's a he, not a she," I said. "The tall man in the blue blazer."

"Oh," the man said. "Okay. See you around." He turned and melted away into the crowd. I gaped after him in complete astonishment. Then I shrugged.

"What's up?" Jack's voice said. He came up alongside me holding a martini in one hand and a bourbon on the rocks in the other. He handed me my drink.

"Thank you," I said, taking a sip of it. "Nothing. I was talking to some guy, and as soon as he found out I was here with a man, he walked away from me."

Jack laughed. "Well, he's in here to meet someone. He's not going to waste time on a woman who's already taken."

"How incredibly flattering to me." I wrinkled my nose. "Jack?"

"Hmmmm?"

I thought for a moment. Then I said, "By *meet someone*, do you mean that a guy like that is looking around here tonight for a woman to—well, to be with?"

"How do you mean, be with?" Jack drank some of his bourbon.

"Well, be with in the sense that you and I are with each other. Is he hoping to run into a woman that he'll really hit it off with so they can have some kind of real relationship?"

"Maybe," Jack said.

I looked at him. "You didn't say that with a great deal of conviction."

"I didn't?"

"No."

He shrugged. "It's sort of hard to say specifically what any one person might have in mind coming to a place like this."

I was still eyeing him. "May I hazard a guess?"

"Certainly."

"Well," I said. "On the basis of the stories I've heard and what I've seen, I'd say that about ninety-nine point nine per cent of the men are here to get laid."

He burst out laughing. "And the women?"

"Also on the basis of what I've heard," I said. "I'd guess that about ninety-nine point nine per cent of *them* are here hoping to meet Prince Charming."

Jack's shoulders were shaking.

"You can laugh, buster," I said sourly. "But it really isn't all that funny."

"What is it, then?"

I paused, looking for the right word. "Depressing," I announced finally. "It's as depressing as all hell."

Jack wasn't laughing anymore. He was looking at me curiously. "Maybe," he said. "Maybe."

I sipped my drink. "Why'd you bring me here tonight?"

He sighed. "Well, it wasn't to depress you, that's for damn sure."

"Seriously. Why?"

Thoughtfully, he gnawed at his lower lip. "Okay," he said. "In the first place, you're observant."

"Thank you. So what?"

"Remember what we were talking about in my office the other day? About a link between Sandra and Joan?"

"Sure."

"Okay. Now—what do you think of the idea that Sandra got snuffed by somebody she picked up in a singles bar?"

I raised my eyebrows. "I'd say it was worth investigating."

"I figured you would. Now put that together with the very big probability that the same guy who killed Sandra, killed Joan."

I stared at him for a moment and then said, "No way, baby."

"No way what?"

I shook my head vigorously. "Uh-uh. If what you're implying is that Joan was running around the bars picking up guys, forget it. *That* I can't buy."

"Why not?"

"Sheesh. She wasn't the *type*, Jack."

He looked as if he were concealing a smile.

"Well, she wasn't," I insisted.

"Do me a favor," he said. "Just try to keep an open mind for the rest of the evening."

I curled my upper lip. "I'll try," I said. "But it won't be easy."

"You can do it."

I was finishing my drink when a subsidiary thought occurred to me. "Jack?"

"Uh-huh?"

"That's really why you brought me here tonight, isn't it?"

"What?"

"To test this, um, theory you have about Joan."

He raised his eyebrows. "Well, that was part of it, yeah. But, like I said before, I really do want you to look around and listen and let me know what you think of this whole scene."

138

"How will that help you find out who killed Joan and Sandy?"

"Because the more we know about the places they hung out, the more we'll know about them," he explained patiently. "And the more we know about them . . ."

He didn't have to finish.

I handed him my empty glass. "Gotcha," I said. "So let's get to it, man."

23

THE NEXT PLACE we went to was called Casablanca, which was underground and dark and cavernous. There was a guard at the door checking I.D.s. On the walls I could make out giant posters—they looked like blown-up movie stills of Humphrey Bogart and Ingrid Bergman. I wondered if the Casablanca were the scene of the beginning of many beautiful friendships. In the mood I was in, I had the feeling not. Sorry, Rick. Sorry, Ilsa.

It was a little hard to tell through the murk, but the crowd here seemed slightly younger and considerably less fearsomely upscale than the one in the Cornucopia. A lot of college kids. Maybe I'd run into one of my former students. That would be a kick.

We only stayed at the Casablanca for about twenty minutes. Time enough, though, for me to down another vodka martini. Jack had a glass of club soda. I looked at it and then at him with raised eyebrows. "No bourbon?"

"Got to keep a clear head," he explained.

"What about me?" I gestured with my glass. "Shouldn't *I* keep a clear head?"

"Nah. Get as wasted as you like. I don't mind having to carry you home."

"What kind of investigator would I be if I got wasted in the midst of my very first investigation?" I demanded. Nonetheless, I drank the martini.

After that, we went to Jonathan Swift's on Boylston Street. I told Jack I hoped the place wasn't called that because it was full of yahoos. He didn't stop laughing for ten minutes. I had another martini, and halfway through it, decided I wasn't having such a bad time after all. Somewhere along the line, I'd apparently abandoned the notion of making this an abstemious evening, although I couldn't remember so doing.

At eleven-thirty we left Jonathan Swift's and walked back up Boylston toward the center of Harvard Square, where Boylston and Brattle and Mass. Avenue intersect.

"Where to now?" I said.

"Feel like walking a bit?" Jack asked. He glanced at my feet. "Can you manage in those shoes? If not we can get a cab."

"No problem," I replied. I stumbled over a frost heave in the sidewalk and grabbed Jack's arm to steady myself.

"I think we ought to get a cab," he said.

"Nonsense," I said. "I'm perfectly capable of walking—how far is it?"

"Four or five blocks."

"No problem," I repeated.

"Mmmm," he said. He didn't sound convinced.

We reached the intersection and turned right onto Mass. Avenue. Harvard Square during the day and early evening is noisy, crowded, dirty, smelly, and exploding with a kind of lunatic vitality that can almost stun you if you're experiencing it for the first time. Approaching midnight, the life and color drain away as if the square were a giant bathtub and someone had just pulled its plug. Most of the people who have a home or at least a place to go have already gone there, or are in the process of going. What remains in the square are the drunks and the druggies and the derelicts and the runaways and the people who prey on the drunks and the druggies and the derelicts and the runaways. Plus an occasional cop.

Despite the cold, it was like that tonight. As we walked past the Cambridge Savings Bank, I saw a figure crouched, head down, in the doorway. I looked closer. It was human, that much I could tell, but its age and sex were indeterminate. It was perfectly motionless and soundless. An apparently living sculpture that someone had draped in khaki-colored down jacket, jeans, and sneakers.

On either side of the bank entranceway were ranged a silent file of adolescent males clad in the standard punk uniform of short leather jackets, jeans, and jack boots. They all had very short hair and tight, expressionless faces. Not even their eyes moved, as far as I could tell. Hands shoved deep into jacket pockets, they looked as if they were guarding the figure crouched in the bank entranceway. Maybe that silent, huddled creature was their leader or god or something.

When we reached the corner of Dunster and Mass. Avenue, I whispered to Jack, "That scares me."

"The neo-Fascist youth movement," he replied. "It scares me, too."

"Let's hurry up," I suggested, "and get to where the bright lights are."

We walked another three blocks, across Bow Street and the intersection of Mass. Avenue and Mount Auburn.

"Where are we going?" I asked. We were passing a big, flossy-looking furniture store that sold the kind of butcher-blocky tables and chairs and couches upper-middle-income Cantabridgians buy to go with polished hardwood floors and antique white walls in renovated three-deckers on Harvard Street. It's a lifestyle I aspire to. Christ.

"Here we are," Jack said.

We stopped in front of a plate-glass-windowed establishment that had a large wooden sign hanging over the entrance. The sign was swaying slightly in the wind and had carved on it, in pseudo-rustic lettering. JIM'S PLACE. There were a lot of hanging plants in the windows.

Jack held the door for me and I preceded him into the joint. I looked around warily. The place was paneled in oak and had a long bar running up the left side of the room. Around the floor were scattered little round or square oak tables with groupings of two and four chairs. Most of the tables were empty, and there were only four or five people at the bar. Well, it was past midnight, and most everyone who'd been here earlier in the evening was probably either off getting laid or busy turning into a pumpkin. The notion of a whole army of sexually frustrated people in Calvin Klein jeans and Ralph Lauren cowboy shirts slowly transforming into large orange gourds made me smile a little.

"Let's sit at the bar for a minute," Jack said.

"Sure."

We hoisted ourselves up side by side on two of the empty stools. I unbuttoned my coat and let it fall open and rested my elbows on the bar. Jack reached into the inside pocket of his blazer and took out a folded white envelope and the little leather case that holds his identification and badge. He set both on the counter in front of him. I looked at them curiously and was about to say something to Jack when the bartender materialized in front of us. The bartender was young, maybe twenty-eight or so, with a round, snub-nosed, Irish face and a Wyatt Earp mustache. He was wearing a blue aviator-style jacket that had "Jim" embroidered in scroll on the breast pocket. The big mustache was wrong on the leprechaun face, like an inept disguise.

The bartender smiled at us with professional bonhomie and said, "What'll it be?"

"A vodka martini on the rocks," Jack said, "and a bourbon on the rocks."

"Right," the bartender said, and moved away to the drink preparation area.

"Are you planning on busting him?" I queried, tilting my head at the bartender's back.

142

"Not unless he waters the drinks," Jack replied. "Why? What put that idea in your head?"

"You have your badge out."

He looked down at the leather case. "Oh. Yeah. No, that's for something else."

"What?"

"Patience," Jack said. "You'll see in a moment."

I rolled my eyes at the ceiling and shook my head.

The bartender came back with our drinks. Jack put some money on the counter. The bartender rang up the sale. He put the change down on the bar and was about to drift off again when Jack said, "Can I talk to you for a minute?"

The bartender halted and gave him a quizzical look. "Something wrong with the drinks, sir?"

Jack shook his head. He opened the badge case and showed the bartender the contents. The bartender studied them for a few seconds and then raised his eyes to look at Jack. Now his face was completely impassive.

"What's the trouble?" he asked.

Jack smiled. "None that I know of," he said pleasantly. "My name is Lingemann. Mind if I ask you a few questions?"

The bartender didn't say anything. But he didn't walk away, either. He remained standing before us, watching Jack very carefully.

Jack opened the envelope and took out a color photograph. I leaned a little closer to him and stared at it. It was a Polaroid shot, close up, of Sandra Dembkoski. She was grinning broadly at the camera and holding aloft a can of Lite. The picture looked as if it had been snapped at a party.

Jack set the photograph on the counter and pushed it toward the bartender with his index finger. The bartender glanced down at it and then back up at Jack. Jack nodded encouragingly. Reluctantly, the bartender picked up the picture and gazed at it.

"Do you know her?" Jack asked.

The bartender was silent, staring at the photograph. Then he set it back down on the counter, carefully, as if it were a very rare and precious daguerreotype of some nineteenth-century celebrity. I noticed he had sucked his upper lip in between his teeth and was chewing the end of his mustache.

"Do you know her?" Jack repeated.

The bartender stopped worrying his mustache and made a faint snorting noise. "Yeah. I know her. I mean, I've seen her around."

"Where around?"

"In here."

"How often?"

The bartender shrugged. "Couple times a week."

"How long's she been coming in?"

The bartender deliberated for a moment. "Maybe three, four months."

"Uh-huh," Jack said. "And what was she here for?"

The bartender threw him a strange look and then gave a brief, unamused laugh. "Same thing they all come in here for, man. She was looking for a guy."

"She have any luck finding one?"

The bartender laughed again. "Oh, yeah. She had a lot of luck, that broad."

Jack nodded. "Ever see her with anyone in particular? I mean, with the same man more than once, say?"

The bartender curled his upper lip. "Are you shitting me, man? That broad was here to get laid. She wasn't looking for no lifetime commitments."

I winced and took a quick sip of my drink. Neither Jack nor the bartender appeared to notice.

"All right," Jack said. He picked up the white envelope and shook out another photograph. It was of Joan Stanley. Here came the acid test for Jack's theory. He handed the picture to the bartender.

"How about this woman?" Jack said. "Ever see her in here? Or anywhere?"

The bartender gazed closely at the photo for about thirty seconds and then set it down alongside the picture of Sandra Dembkoski. I waited, holding my breath.

"Yeah," the bartender said. "Seen that one in here a lot, too."

I let out my pent-up breath as softly as possible.

"What can you tell me about her?" Jack asked.

The bartender shrugged. "She was in here for the same reason as the other one. To pick up something."

"Did she?" Jack said.

"Yeah."

"And?"

The bartender shrugged again. "What else is there to say? She'd come in, have a couple of glasses of something, look the crowd over, spot some guy, and hit on him. They'd have a couple more drinks and leave together."

"Ever see her with the same guy twice?"

144

"Nope."

"Uh-huh. You know any of the guys she or the other one"—Jack nodded at the photo of Sandra—"went with?"

The bartender was silent, gazing at Jack. Jack looked back at him, quite steadily. I took another sip of my drink, pretending to be uninterested in the proceedings. I wasn't sure what my role in this little drama was supposed to be.

"Ah, *shit*," the bartender said softly. He heaved a deep sigh.

"I'm waiting," Jack said. His voice was still calm and pleasant, but there was a faint undertone of warning in it.

The bartender took a cloth from beneath the counter and began polishing the bar top slowly, methodically. When he spoke again, his lips barely moved. I had to strain to catch what he was saying.

"Look, man," the bartender said. "I start talking about my customers to cops, and what happens to my business?"

Jack put his right elbow on the counter top and rested his chin on his hand. He grinned at the bartender and said, "Nothing nearly as bad as what'll happen to it if I decide to start looking for building code violations in this herpes hacienda."

I laughed midway through a swallow of vodka and vermouth, gagged, and started to cough. Without taking his eyes off the bartender, Jack reached up with his left hand and patted me on the back. I wiped my mouth with a cocktail napkin, still giggling uncontrollably.

The bartender wasn't as amused. "Oh, fuck me," he said. He gave a final swipe to the counter top with the damp cloth, balled it up, and tossed it under the bar. He dug into his jacket pocket, fished out a package of Marlboros, and lit one with abrupt, angry motions. He took a deep drag on the cigarette and blew a long plume of smoke over Jack's left shoulder. Then he leaned forward slightly.

"I seen that one"—the bartender indicated the picture of Joan—"with one guy who comes in here pretty regular."

"He here tonight?" Jack asked.

The bartender hesitated a moment and then nodded, a single up and down movement of the head.

"He here now?" Jack asked.

The bartender tapped his cigarette into an ashtray on the counter. "Over in the back corner," he said softly. "The one in the blue sweater."

I restrained myself from glancing even casually to my right.

"Okay, good," Jack said. "What about the other woman? You ever see her with anyone you know?"

"Oh, man, what the hell you think I do in here?" the bartender expostulated. "Fix people up? How do I know who that broad was with? She was all over anything in pants came in here."

"Uh-huh," Jack said. He reached into his pocket and took out one of his cards. He handed it to the bartender. The bartender took it without even glancing at it and put it under the bar.

"If you remember anything about what I want to know," Jack said, "call me at the number on that card."

"Yeah, sure, okay," the bartender said.

Jack picked up his bourbon and tasted it. Nearly all the ice in the glass had melted and the drink was the color of chablis. The bartender didn't offer to get Jack a fresh bourbon.

"Appreciate all your help," Jack said.

"Yeah, right," the bartender said.

Jack set his glass down on the counter and gave the man a big, unfriendly grin. "I'll be back again soon with more questions."

"Yeah," the bartender said. "Don't do me no favors, huh?"

24

THE BARTENDER MOVED to the opposite end of the bar and busied himself polishing glasses. I suspected he'd grown tired of our company.

"Soul of cooperation, wasn't he?" I murmured to Jack.

Jack smiled a little. "Spilled his guts all over the bar," he agreed.

"Now what?"I said.

"Let's relocate," Jack said. He got off the bar stool. "Bring your drink." He picked up his watery bourbon and raised it to me in a small salute. Then he began sauntering toward the rear of the room. It didn't take much effort to figure out where he was heading.

I grabbed my martini glass, slid off the bar stool, and followed him to the table at which the man in the blue sweater sat. The man glanced up in vague surprise when he saw the two of us approaching him. There was a half-empty schooner of beer on the table in front of him.

"Mind if we join you?" Jack asked. Without waiting for an answer, he pulled out a chair for me and took one himself.

The man in the blue sweater looked uneasily from Jack to me and back again. I studied him. He was probably around thirty and handsome in a sort of Jack Armstrong All-American-Boy way. Blond hair and blue eyes. A good healthy color, though that could have been the rosy blush of much beer consumption. Probably tall, judging by the length of his back and the breadth of his shoulders.

"Do I know either of you?" the man said, his eyes still flicking back and forth between us.

"Don't believe so," Jack said easily. He took out his leather I.D. case, flipped it open, and showed it to the man. "My name is Lingemann, and I'd like—"

The man in the blue sweater pushed back his chair and started to rise. Like lightning, Jack reached up, grabbed him by the shoulder, and shoved him back in the chair. I sucked in an involuntary sharp breath. Jack gave me a slight reassuring smile and then turned back to face the man in the blue sweater. His hand was still clamped on the guy's shoulder. A couple at a table about ten feet away glanced at us curiously and then looked away quickly.

"In a hurry to get someplace?" Jack inquired placidly.

The man slumped in his chair and glowered at the table top, saying nothing.

"That wasn't very bright," Jack continued. "Getting up like that. It makes me think you have something against cops. Am I right about that?"

The man remained silent. Jack's hand seemed to tighten on his shoulder.

"Oh, Christ," the man said. "Will you lighten up?"

Jack and I were getting a real warm reception at Jim's Place tonight. So far we were two for two with the owner and the patrons. Everyone just loved us to pieces.

"What's your name?" Jack said.

"Francis," the guy muttered.

"Francis what?"

"Danny Francis."

"Okay, Danny," Jack said. "That's better. Now—you want to take it from the top again?"

Francis shrugged. His face was sullen. The expression curdled the boyish good looks the way a squirt of lemon juice will sour cream.

"Right," Jack said. He took his hand from Francis's shoulder and leaned back a little in his seat, looking relaxed and almost off-guard. I wasn't fooled by the pose. If Francis had had any previous experience with cops, he wouldn't be, either.

Francis made no move to rise. Instead, he picked up his glass and swallowed about half the beer remaining in it.

Jack took the picture of Joan Stanley from his pocket and set it on the table in front of Francis.

"You know this woman?" Jack asked.

"No," Francis said, without looking at the photograph.

"That's interesting," Jack said. "I heard otherwise."

"Yeah, well, you heard shit," Francis replied.

There was a few seconds' silence. Then Jack sighed. "Look, Francis," he said in tones of great reasonableness. "There're a number of ways this can be done. It's late and I'm tired and I'd just as soon keep it easy. Okay?"

"Fuck you," Francis said. A real charmer.

"Jesus," Jack said. He shook his head slowly. Then he reached across the table, grabbed a handful of Francis's sweater front, and yanked. Francis rose halfway out of his seat, his eyes wide with shock. He was a big guy and probably not used to being shoved. Or dragged out of chairs.

148

"Look at the picture, asshole," Jack said. He let go of Francis's sweater and Francis fell back in his chair. Hard. It rocked, nearly toppled over, and then steadied. Francis grabbed the edge of the table and took a deep breath. He shot Jack a look that was five eighths loathing and three eighths defiance. But he was also nervous; even I could sense that. Maybe it was all the experience I'd had confronting students with plagiarized term papers.

Francis and Jack had a staring contest that lasted for about forty-five seconds. Francis lost. His gaze dropped to the table top.

"Look at the picture," Jack said inexorably.

Francis sat very still for a few moments. Then he let out a long sigh and mumbled, "Shit." It was dawning on him that he was out of his weight class, so to speak. He picked up the picture and glanced at it. I watched his face closely. He did a very slight double-take as he looked at the photo, nothing you would have noticed if you hadn't been looking for it, and dropped the picture on the table top.

"Well?" Jack said. He was leaning back in his chair again, looking easy and relaxed.

"Yeah," Francis said. "I know her."

"Okay," Jack said. He reached into his pocket and took out the picture of Sandra Dembkoski. He handed it to Francis. Francis took it and stared at it dully.

"How about her?" Jack said. "She look familiar to you?"

Francis hesitated a moment and then made a gesture of assent. There didn't seem to be any resistance left in him. Funny. Jack hadn't pressed him *that* hard. Oh, well. Some people just caved in quicker than others.

"You know the both of them, then," Jack said.

Francis shrugged with one shoulder.

"Is that yes or no?"

"Yeah."

"Okay. You seen either one recently?"

"Whaddya mean?"

"I mean," Jack said patiently, "have you seen either of those women recently?"

"Oh." Francis frowned, thinking. I got the impression that his I.Q. wasn't up there in the Einstein range. "No."

"No?"

Francis rubbed the side of his face with his left hand. He glanced at the picture of Joan Stanley. "That one," he said. "Last I saw her was, oh, hell, I don't know. Maybe a month ago. Something like that. Who knows?"

"How about the Sunday before last?" Jack said. "You see her then?"

"Huh?"

"A week ago Sunday."

Francis shook his head. "No."

"Okay. What happened the last time you saw her?"

"That was the *only* time I saw her, man."

"Uh-huh. What happened?"

Francis shot me a quick look. "You know," he said to Jack.

"No, I don't," Jack replied. "Tell me."

"Oh, Christ," Francis said. "I was in here one night and she came up to me and started talking. That's all. Jesus."

"Go on," Jack said.

Francis swallowed the last of his beer. "So we talked."

"What'd you talk about?"

Francis scowled. "Oh, man, I don't know. The usual shit."

"What about after that?"

"What about it?"

Jack closed his eyes for a moment. Then he opened them and said, "Francis, don't bullshit me. You and the girl left this place together. Where'd you go? Her place? Yours?"

"Oh, Christ," Francis said. "Mine. It was closer."

"What happened when you got there?"

"Oh, man, what do you think happened? We fucked. Jesus."

"What about later?"

"She went home, man. She got up, got dressed, called a cab, and left."

"Okay. Ever see her after that?"

"No. I mean, yeah, I saw her in here a couple times. But . . ." Francis's voice trailed off and he shrugged.

"What's that mean?" Jack asked.

Francis shook his head. "So I saw her. I said hello to her. She said hello to me. She was with somebody else. I don't think she even recognized me."

I swigged down the last of my martini. Oddly, I no longer felt the least bit drunk. Instead, I felt like getting another martini. Urgently. It was the uplifting quality of the dialogue I was listening to, I think.

"Okay," Jack said. He picked up the picture of Sandra Dembkoski. "What about her?"

Francis glanced at the photograph. "Oh, Christ, that tramp," he said.

"When'd you see her last?"

"In here?" Francis shrugged again. "Maybe a week ago."

"Ever see her anywhere else?"

150

"No."

"You ever get together with her?"

Francis laughed. It was a nasty sound. "Not me, man. I like something with a little more class than that."

"Yeah," Jack said. "You got so much yourself."

"Huh?" Francis was definitely not quick on the uptake.

"Never mind," Jack said wearily. "Just tell me what you were doing Tuesday night."

"Tuesday night?"

"Yeah. Tuesday night. The one before last. Tuesday. It comes between Monday and Wednesday, you know?"

Francis ruminated. "Visiting a friend," he said finally.

"What friend was that?"

Francis looked at Jack. "What the hell difference does it make?"

"Who were you with, Francis?"

"Like I said. A friend."

Jack leaned forward. "Francis, I am getting sort of impatient with you. I want the name of the friend you were visiting."

In a sudden swift motion Francis put his hands under the rim of the table and yanked it upward sharply. The three glasses on it slid toward me and sailed into the air. My martini glass and Jack's bourbon glass fell to the floor and shattered. The beer schooner hit me in the solar plexus. I gasped and pulled back, just in time to avoid having the table land in my lap. It crashed to the floor with an appalling thud, barely missing my left foot. Francis was out of his seat and running for the door. There was a feminine-sounding shriek from somewhere behind me.

What happened next all seemed to take place in slow motion. Jack was up and after Francis while the glasses were still flying through the air. He caught up with him halfway down the bar, in a kind of tackle. The two of them landed on the floor with an impact that made the rows of bottles behind the bar rattle and clink together. I closed my eyes. Francis was a 4-H creep, but if Jack were going to pound him into steak tartare, I didn't especially want to watch.

When I opened my eyes, Jack was standing over me, looking concerned. "Are you okay?" he asked.

I nodded and glanced down at my dress front. There was some residual beer foam clinging to my cleavage. I got a tissue from my handbag and dabbed it away. "I'm fine."

Jack nodded and sank into the one other chair that had remained upright. He straightened his tie. "Well, there's one good thing about all this."

I looked at him curiously. "What's that?"

He gave a tired laugh. "I promised you a colorful evening, didn't I?"

I crumpled my tissue and let it fall to the floor. "Oh, yeah," I said. "And you *never* break a promise."

25

DANNY FRANCIS, WHATEVER else he had or hadn't done, had nothing to do with either Joan Stanley or Sandra Dembkoski getting killed. The results of the autopsy on Sandra made that much, at least, quite clear. Like Joan, Sandra had died, to quote the medical examiner's report, "from multiple blows to the skull with a sharp, heavy instrument." The wounds were not inconsistent with the kind that might be inflicted by a small axe or a claw hammer. Or maybe, I reflected, even the sharp, flat base of a cast-iron statue.

Like Joan, Sandra had been raped, probably repeatedly, almost certainly at least once after her death, with a kind of methodical savagery belied by the medical examiner's dry, matter-of-fact prose. Jack let me read the whole document, but I had to skip over that part of it. The first two lines describing the nature and extent of the lacerations made me sick.

Whoever killed the women had type A blood.

The bite marks on the women were identical.

In other words, Joan and Sandra had been murdered by the same man.

It wasn't Francis. His blood type was O. His bite mark bore absolutely no resemblance to the casts of the ones taken from the bodies of the two women.

Francis *did* have a criminal record, but it was strictly small-time, and not for any kind of sex-related offense. He'd been arrested twice, the first time in Boston three years ago for drunken driving. The second arrest, two years later, also in Boston, was for something heavier. Francis was picked up outside a bar on Tremont Street and charged with possession of cocaine with intent to distribute. Francis was lucky. The charge against him was dropped, ultimately, because the evidence in the case "disappeared" from the police property office. Cute.

Francis hadn't been in any trouble recently. At any rate, none that had come to the attention of the authorities.

"So what was his problem, then?" I said to Jack. "Why did he try to bolt when you asked him what he'd been doing the night Sandra got murdered?"

"I didn't ask him what he was doing the night Sandra got murdered. I asked him what he was doing Tuesday night."

I crossed my eyes and made a faint sound of exasperation. "Yeah, right. Well?"

Jack smiled. "Well, like he said, he was visiting a friend."

"Uh-huh. What friend?"

"Somebody the Lynn and state cops have had their eye on for about six months now."

"Oh?" I raised my eyebrows. "For what?"

Jack finished his coffee before replying. He set the cup in the saucer. "Guy's one of the bigger drug distributors for the North Shore."

"Oh," I repeated. "No *wonder* Francis didn't want to tell you where he was." I shook my head and laughed a little scornfully. "What a jerk, though. To try to run like that, I mean. You had nothing on him. If he'd had half a brain, he'd have just sat there and stonewalled you." I made a palms-up gesture with both hands. "Instead he got an all-expense-paid trip to police headquarters and a personal tour of an interrogation room. Schmuck."

"He didn't seem to be overly endowed in terms of intellect," Jack agreed. "But then, not many of them are. You don't run across a lot of genius criminals. I don't, anyway. Course, there's always a first time."

The waitress tittupped over to the table and asked us if we would care for more coffee.

"Liz?" Jack said.

I smiled at the waitress and shook my head.

"Just the check," Jack added.

I looked at my watch. It was eleven-thirty. Having dinner out in the Boston–Cambridge area on a Friday evening can be a protracted business. We didn't do it very often, mostly because neither of us enjoys waiting hours to get a table, which you always end up doing even if you have a reservation. Jack hates it even more than I do. Tonight had been his idea, though. I think he was trying to make amends for the previous evening.

Jack paid the bill. We got our coats from the checkroom and walked to the car. It was a nice night, clear and still and not quite as bone-chillingly cold as it had been earlier in the week. Thanksgiving was thirteen days away.

"What next?" Jack said.

"Good heavens," I said in mock surprise. "You mean you haven't any bars lined up for us to go to?"

He grinned. "Someone else is working that detail tonight."

154

"Damn," I said. "I was really looking forward to another hour or so of watching you harass and intimidate slobs."

"Maybe another time," he replied.

"I'll hold you to that," I said.

We got to the car. Jack unlocked and opened the passenger door. I slid onto the front seat, tucking my coat around me. He went around to the driver's side.

"So," he said. "Where to?"

"My house," I said promptly. "I was thinking it might be fun to sit in front of the fire and drink brandy and watch the flames and, you know, stuff."

"Jesus, what a romantic you are," Jack said.

"I know," I said. "It's one of my worst failings." I glanced at him out of the corner of my eye. "Yours, too, darlin'. That's why you're a cop."

Even in the dark I could see him smile.

Going down Mass. Avenue we passed Jim's Place. Even through the tinted plate glass windows, and from the not-ideal vantage point of a moving car, I could see that it was packed. Well, Friday night was a hot one on the singles circuit, or so I'd heard. I sighed.

"What's the matter?" Jack said.

"Nothing. Fleeting thought."

"About what?"

"Jim's Place. We just passed it."

"Oh."

We drove another few blocks in silence. Then I said, "Jack?"

"Yes?"

I turned a little on the seat to look at him. "Did anybody you talked to about Joan, her friends or whatever, even hint to you that she might be— uh, screwing around?"

"Nope."

I shook my head slowly. "Just like Lisa Waite carefully neglecting to tell you how Joan was messing around with Bingham. Speak no evil and all that."

"Yeah, maybe. Or maybe they just didn't know about it. That's possible, too, you know."

"I suppose," I said. "God! The secret life of Joan Stanley."

We turned onto my street. Jack parked the car in front of my house. We got out and walked up the path to the front porch. I took my keycase from my purse and flipped it open. We went up the steps.

I didn't need the key. The front door was ajar about an inch.

"Dammit," I said, practically stamping my foot. "Will you look at that?" I pointed at the door.

"Your upstairs neighbor," Jack said. "The Quaalude Kid."

"Who else?" I replied furiously.

"Probably," Jack said. "Still, I'll go in first." He pushed open the front door, stepped into the foyer, and glanced around him. Then he started up the staircase to the second floor. I noticed he had unbuttoned his sheepskin coat. Not because it was excessively warm in the building. It's just that should you have to, it's sort of hard to draw a gun through a closed jacket.

I waited about thirty seconds and then followed him. If someone hadn't been murdered in this building less than two weeks ago, I'd have said we were being absurdly overcautious. The chances that the downstairs door was open for any reason other than that my idiot upstairs neighbor had gone in or out and neglected to shut it behind him were infinitesimal. But . . .

I joined Jack outside my apartment door. It was locked, just the way I'd left it a few hours ago.

"Give me your key," Jack said.

I handed him the key and retreated about five feet. I stood with my back to the corridor wall as he unlocked the door. The moment he opened it, Lucy leaped over the threshold, tail wagging frenetically. She jumped up on Jack, and I burst out laughing. Jack gave her a quick pat on the head and stepped over the threshold into the living room. Lucy darted over to me and planted her forepaws on my thighs, giving me a big canine grin of welcome.

It doesn't take all that long to check out a three-room apartment for intruders. A minute or so later, Jack called back to me, "Come on in."

I walked into the living room. Jack had hung up his coat and was sitting on the couch.

"That was a lot of unnecessary drama, wasn't it?" I said.

He shrugged.

I took off my coat. "Start the fire," I said. "I'll get the booze."

"Yes, ma'am," Jack said. "Right away. God, I love strong-minded women."

"Who doesn't?" I said, and went to the kitchen.

When I returned to the living room with the applejack bottle and the glasses, Jack was on the floor in front of the fireplace, setting a log on the grate. I put the glasses and liquor on the coffee table and sat down next to him. He crumpled some newspaper and stuffed it under the grate.

"Got a match?"

156

I nodded. "There's some in that little box on the mantelpiece." I reached up, retrieved the matches, and tossed them to Jack. He caught them and struck one and touched it to the newspaper. I turned to pour us some brandy.

I handed Jack a glass and we settled down side by side, our shoulders touching. The flames flared up from the newspaper and licked at the ends of the logs. I glanced at Jack. He was staring at the fire, looking pensive. I could guess what was on his mind. The same thing that had been on it for the past twelve days. I leaned a bit closer to him and he put his arm around me. I slid a hand underneath his jacket and began rubbing his back in big, slow circles. He turned a little and rested his chin on the top of my head.

One of the logs made a loud popping noise. We watched it explode in a tiny shower of sparks, our own private miniature pyrotechnic display. Lucy wandered into the room and, after a brief survey of the scene, plopped down on the rug a few feet away, her muzzle resting on her forepaws. In a few moments, her eyes began to close.

"So," I said presently. "What did you do with yourself today?"

"You asking me or the dog?" Jack replied.

I smiled. "You. I *know* what Lucy did. Same thing she always does. Get up, go out, take a nap, chew on her bone, take a nap, get a drink, take a nap, go out, work on the bone some more, take a nap, have dinner, get a drink, go out, take a nap, and do some more with the bone."

"Uh-huh. My schedule wasn't that varied."

"Oh. Well, that's the way it goes sometimes. So how *did* you spend the day?"

He yawned. "Interviewing some of the, ah, boyfriends, I guess you'd call them, of Sandra."

"Oh, Lord," I said, and took a sip of my drink. "How did that go?"

Jack shrugged. "Well, I don't think any of them killed her or Joan, if that's what you mean."

I set my glass down on the rug. "Did any of these guys, um—know Joan, too?"

He smiled a little at my choice of words. "They claimed not to. So far, there's nothing to connect any of them with her."

I shook my head. "Maybe Joan was a little more discriminating in her selection of partners than Sandy was." I paused, suddenly aware of the contradiction in what I was saying. "Although . . ."

Jack gave me a questioning look. "Although what?"

"Well," I said slowly. "I would seriously debate the standards of anybody who'd sleep with a slug like Danny Francis."

"Like the man said," Jack replied, "she wasn't looking for a lifetime commitment."

"Yeah," I said sourly. "Only for a—how was it you put it? Oh, right. 'One fleeting night of ecstasy.' Augh." I picked up my drink. "Jesus, ecstasy in the arms of Danny Francis, can you dig that?" I took another swallow of the applejack. "So what else can you tell me? About Sandra, I mean?"

Instead of replying, Jack took off the coat to his suit and tossed it on the couch. He loosened his tie and unbuttoned the top two buttons of his shirt. Then he stretched out on the floor, his hands behind his head.

"With all that preparation," I commented, "what you're about to say must be a real wowser."

He laughed. "Not really. Just wanted to get comfortable."

"So? What is it?" I leaned toward him.

"Well," Jack said. He broke off speaking, picked up his glass, and drank from it. Then he set the glass down carefully on the hearth tiles. When he spoke again, his tone was reflective, almost abstracted. "You know, the thing that sticks with me is that I don't think I've ever, as long as I can remember doing this, seen such an accumulation of different fingerprints as there were in Sandra's apartment. In her bedroom."

I stared at him over the rim of my glass. "I bet," I said.

"God," he continued. "There were, oh, twenty-seven distinct sets anyway." He shook his head. "And they haven't finished separating them yet. So there's probably more. Christ only knows who they belong to. None of them match up with any on file. Oh, well. At least she wasn't consorting with any known felons."

"Sure had a lot of company, didn't she?" I said. "Little Sandra."

"Yeah. Kind of depressing to think about, isn't it? I mean, a kid that age."

"It's depressing," I said flatly, "for a kid anyone's age." I finished my applejack and poured myself another. I took a substantial swallow of it and set the glass on my knee. I stared at the fire.

After a moment, Jack said, "This really bothers you, doesn't it?"

I looked over at him. "What makes you think that?"

He laughed. "Honey, you should see your expression."

I rubbed a hand over my face, as if to wipe away whatever look was there. Then I let out a long sigh and shrugged. It was a gesture of concession. "Yeah, you're right. It bothers the hell out of me."

"Like the other night," Jack said. "In the bar."

I nodded. "Sort of."

"What is it?"

I drank some applejack. "Ooohhh, I don't know. I guess—I can't figure it out, that's all. *Understand* it. It makes no sense to me."

Jack was looking at me quite intently now. "What makes no sense?"

"Sandra and Joan." I shook my head. "Why'd they do what they did? Why go to a bar, hit on some guy, bring him home, and screw him? Why?" I took a deep breath. "What can anybody get out of something like that? A half-drunk fuck with someone she doesn't know, probably doesn't want to know, doesn't like, who almost certainly has no regard for her, and whom she'll almost certainly never see again. That's nice? That's good? That's self-respecting? That's even fun, for Christ's sake?" I drained my glass and set it down on the hearth with a sharp click.

"Damned if I know," Jack said lightly.

I gave him as hard a look as I could manage. He smiled and reached up and patted my shoulder. "Don't get so wound up about it," he said. "It's ugly, I know, especially the way you put it, but . . . why let it get to you that way? Anyhow"—he took his hand from my shoulder and made a palms-up gesture—"maybe Joan and Sandra saw the whole thing differently from you. Maybe to them it was like, I don't know, some kind of romantic adventure."

I poured myself some more applejack. "Maybe," I said. "And maybe that was what got them killed."

26

THE ONLY ILL effect I suffered from the consumption of three hefty
glasses of applejack, plus the two vodka martinis before dinner and the
wine during, was a somewhat parched mouth the following morning. Two
glasses of orange juice took care of that. My liver I could neither see nor
feel, which was probably all to the good. In any case, I was in A-1 shape.
Perhaps Bacchus looks after his own.

After I dressed and had breakfast, I got the phone book and looked up
the number of the Inman Square Crisis and Counseling Center. I dialed it.
The person who answered the phone confirmed for me that, yes, the center
was open on Saturdays from twelve to four, and yes, the assistant director
would be available. No, I didn't need to make an appointment to see him.
Just drop in at any point during the afternoon.

Very good. I hung up the phone and looked at the clock on the end table.
It was just noon. Lucy trotted into the room and positioned herself directly
in front of me, giving me one of those wistful yet diffident gee-I-really-
hate-to-inconvenience-you-but-I'd-really-like-to-go-outside looks.

"Sure," I said. When she saw me head for the closet to get my coat, her
ears stiffened with excitement and she capered over to the front door. It
was charming, I thought as we left the apartment, to be able to so easily
gratify the dearest wish of another sentient being.

At twelve-fifteen, I was on my way to the Inman Square Crisis and
Counseling Center. I walked, despite the fact that Inman Square was a
little over two miles from where I lived and that the temperature was
hovering somewhere around a distinctly unbalmy twenty-five degrees. But
I wanted the exercise, and anyway, if I waited for a bus, I'd probably die
of exposure long before one finally came along.

As I picked my way along the narrow, twisting side streets, my mind
returned to Joan and Sandra. I was very nearly convinced, now, that they'd
been killed by some attractive closet psychotic they'd unwittingly picked
up in some bar. God only knew there was plenty of precedent for that. Mr.
Goodbar was legion. In the Cambridge–Boston area itself, about ten or
twelve years ago, there'd been a series of particularly revolting rape and

torture murders of young women, mostly college students. *That* case got solved, but only after two years and after nine girls had been stabbed, strangled, shot, or beaten to death. What ultimately linked all the victims, and led the police to their murderer, was the fact that each young woman had been a frequenter of dating bars. Their murderer? A well-spoken, intelligent, avuncular man they'd met in a bar who'd offered to escort them home at closing time so they wouldn't have to chance the streets alone. He'd hit on a foolproof way to inspire their trust and confidence. He'd posed as an off-duty Cambridge police detective. He'd even had the stolen badge and service revolver to prove it.

So perhaps something similar had happened to Joan and Sandra.

A logical enough assumption. Yet it troubled me vaguely, and I couldn't pinpoint why. There was a flaw in it somewhere. Some fact about the case, that I was sure I'd known before but had simply forgotten, that didn't jibe with the notion that Sandra and Joan had been killed by a one-time pick-up.

Preoccupied as I was by these thoughts, I nearly walked straight through Inman Square. I *did* manage to walk right past the counseling center. Feeling a bit silly, I backtracked half a block.

The empty domestic port bottle that had lent a jolly informal decorator touch to the exterior of the building the last time I'd been here was gone, but some graffiti artist, feeling perhaps a need to compensate for the lack, had thoughtfully substituted his or her own aesthetic signature. Whoever it was went in heavily for humor *noire*. On the lower half of the door was scribbled, in black felt-tipped marker, "Have a nice day, asshole."

When I stopped laughing, I pushed open the door and walked into the center. The same frizzy-haired young receptionist was seated at the foremost desk, still rattling away at her typewriter. She didn't glance up at my approach. I cleared my throat and shuffled my feet. She looked up at me. I smiled. She didn't.

"Help you?" she asked, in her Cambridgeport whine.

"Is Peter Lewis in?" I said.

"Yeah," she said. She turned her head to the left about forty-seven degrees and screamed, "Hey, Peeeeeter." I winced, and wondered what effect that bottle-shattering voice might have on the more psychically fragile of the center's clientele.

A moment later, Lewis emerged from his cubbyhole. "Jesus, Diane," he was saying exasperatedly. "Can't you—" He broke off when he noticed me. "Oh," he said, sounding surprised. Then he smiled. "Hello."

"Hi," I responded.

He stood in the doorway of his office, one hand resting on the doorjamb. "You're here to see me."

It was a question, not a statement. I nodded.

"Come in," he said. He remained in the doorway, his posture relaxed and casual.

I wound my way through the ranks of battered metal desks and molded plastic chairs to his cubbyhole.

"Nice to see you again," Lewis said.

I smiled. "You too."

"Come in," Lewis repeated. "Sit down." He pushed himself away from the doorjamb and backed into the office, so that there was room for me to enter without having to squeeze past him.

I parked myself in the same chair I'd occupied during my previous visit. Lewis took the chair behind the desk and tilted it back so that the very top was resting against the rear office wall. He clasped his hands behind his head. The pose swelled the muscles in his upper arms and tensed the long muscles in his forearms. He looked strong. I wondered if he worked out with weights. I would have felt silly asking.

"So," Lewis said. "What's new?"

I started a little, realizing that I had been staring at him with the same bland smile for a good thirty seconds.

I widened the smile to a grin. "I need help," I said.

"Yes," Lewis replied, straightfaced. "Funny how nearly everyone I talk to in the course of the day says the same thing to me."

"Not *that* kind of help," I said, snickering. "At least, not at the moment, anyway."

"Oh." Lewis nodded. "That's good. So what kind of help *do* you need?"

I shifted around in the narrow, rickety chair, trying to find a comfortable position. "Remember the article I was writing on Joan Stanley?"

"Sure."

"Well, there've been some new developments," I said. "Nothing good, unfortunately."

He frowned a little. "What's happened?"

"Another woman got murdered Tuesday night," I said flatly. "The cops think she got killed by the same guy who killed Joan."

Lewis's frown turned to a grimace. "Oh, yeah, I heard about that. Jesus."

"Yes," I replied. "It's pretty bad." How trite the understatement sounded.

Lewis rubbed his right hand over his face and then exhaled slowly. "Do the cops have any idea who did it?"

162

"Nope." I slipped out of my jacket and hung it over the arm of my chair. "Not that I know of."

"That's awful," Lewis said.

"Yeah," I agreed. Better terse than trite.

Shaking his head slowly, Lewis rose from behind his desk. "I was just going to have some coffee," he said. "Can I get you some?"

"Okay. Thank you."

"You're welcome. How do you take it?"

"The works."

He smiled a little at that and left the office. Alone, I tried to marshal my thoughts. I had a number of questions to ask Lewis, and I hoped I wouldn't forget any of them. I reached into my handbag and fished out my little notebook and pen.

Lewis returned to the office carrying two steaming Styrofoam cups of coffee. He handed me one and said, "There you go." Then he resumed his seat behind the desk.

"So," he said, blowing across the top of his cup to cool its contents. "What kind of help is it you're looking for?"

I set my cup on the edge of the desk and took a deep breath. There was little to be gained from pussyfooting around the issue. "I want you to tell me," I said, "what kind of man you think might be responsible for committing these crimes."

Lewis didn't move so much as an eyelid, but sat quietly in his chair, contemplating me over the top of his coffee cup. He didn't look taken aback, merely mildly curious. Then he said, "Are you asking me for a profile?"

"Well, yes," I said. "That, or—or any kind of speculation you might be able to offer."

Lewis's eyebrows went up. "I'm not a psychiatrist, you know," he replied.

"I know," I said. "But . . ." My voice trailed off and I looked at him appealingly.

"Well," Lewis said dubiously, "I really question whether *my* speculations would be of any use to you."

His diffidence was a refreshing contrast to the arrogance of Christopher Bingham.

"Come on," I urged. "You must have some ideas on the subject."

Lewis fell silent again for a few moments, sipping his coffee. The space between his eyebrows was puckered in thought, as if he were giving my request hard consideration. I opened my notebook.

"Okay," he said finally. "I *do* have a couple of ideas."

I sat back, pen poised over a blank page in the notebook.

"Before I start," Lewis said, "I have to tell you that I really don't have a lot of faith in this sort of thing."

I blinked at him in some surprise. "In psychiatric profiles?"

"Uh-huh."

I was intrigued. How many shrinks do you know who go around disclaiming their omniscience, or the infallibility of their methods? "Why not?"

Lewis shrugged. "Lots of reasons. Mostly, though, it's that I don't think they have any practical use."

"Really?" I was reminded of Jack's comments on the subject.

"Sure." Lewis put his feet on the desk. "How can they have any? Even if they're accurate, which only happens maybe half the time, all they do is identify a type."

"What's wrong with that?" I said.

"That's the whole problem," he replied. "Don't you see?"

"Well, no. You'll have to explain it to me." Actually, I was pretty sure I agreed with Lewis about the value of profiles; I just wanted to hear the rest of his objections to them.

"For one thing," Lewis said, "when the police are looking for a killer, they're looking for a specific person, right? Well, the profile's not going to single that guy out for them. It may fit ten people, it may fit two hundred, a hundred and ninety-nine of whom the worst thing they ever did was to get a parking ticket. So . . ." He spread his hands to express the hopelessness of the situation.

I nodded my acknowledgment of the point. "Okay. But remember that whatever you tell me today I'm only going to use as speculation in the thing I'm writing. I'm not going to use it to try to track down a mass murderer."

"Serial murderer," Lewis corrected. "There's a difference. Mass murderers are those guys who get up on highway overpasses with sniper rifles and wipe out fifteen people at once."

"Right." I glanced down at my empty notebook as if seeking inspiration there. "Serial killers. Is there any kind of generalization you can make about a person like that?"

Lewis pinched his lower lip between his thumb and forefinger, ruminating. "Well," he said slowly. "I can tell you right off that I've never heard of one who had a happy childhood. I mean they all seem to have experienced some kind of severe abuse or trauma at an early age."

I wrote down his response in my notebook. "I thought that was true of criminals in general. Not just serial murderers."

"It is, as a matter of fact," Lewis said dryly. "You see what I mean about profiles?"

I had to laugh. "Yes."

"So should I go on?"

"Of course," I replied. I paused, thinking. "You know, I heard another psychiatrist talk about this recently. He had some very definite ideas about the kind of person that might have killed Joan and this other woman, Sandra Dembkoski."

"Oh?" Lewis looked interested. "What were they?"

I gave him a recap of the gospel according to Christopher Bingham, concluding with an explanation of my doubts that the kind of man Bingham had described would stand a chance of even striking up a conversation with two women like Sandra and Joan, much less of getting them home and into bed. Lewis listened to me with great attention, occasionally giving a thoughtful nod.

When I finished my spiel, he said, "That sounds reasonable."

I assumed he was referring to my doubts. "I thought so, too." I said.

"Although," Lewis continued, "you can't totally discount everything this—Bingham, did you say his name was?"

I nodded.

"Yeah, well, part of that profile he gave you might be accurate. Another part might not be. There's no way of knowing until they catch the killer." Lewis sipped his coffee.

I picked up my own cup and sampled the contents. I'd heard of Colombian coffee. This was pre-Colombian. I set the cup back on the edge of the desk, away from me. "Okay," I said. "So you're telling me, then, that serial murderers don't all belong to the same personality type. Right?"

"Absolutely," Lewis replied. "There're probably as many different personality types among serial killers as there are serial killers."

"What a charming thought," I said, making a note of the comment in my little book. "What about the, um, psychiatric disorders they suffer from?" I was pleased with the clinical phrasing of the question. "Are there any similarities there?"

"This isn't really my area of expertise," Lewis said. "But, on the basis of what I've read, I'd have to say there was no way to generalize about that, either. Although . . ."

"Yes?" I hunched forward in my chair.

"Well," he said, with some considerable distaste. "Serial killers who go after women get off on beating and torturing and raping their victims. I guess you could call that a similarity. Or a pattern."

"I guess you could," I said. "The creep who killed Sandra and Joan did all those things." I tapped my pen against the spine of the notebook. "He also seems to have been a necrophiliac. Does that make him unique? Or even unusual?"

"Oh, no. I read of a case—in fact, I think I have the book here—of a guy in New Mexico who killed eleven women and *then* raped and sodomized them."

"Jesus," I said, grimacing. "What was *his* problem?"

Instead of replying, Lewis leaned sideways in his chair and pulled a heavy-looking volume with a ragged blue dust jacket from the bookcase to the right of his desk. He heaved the book into his lap and began riffling through it, pausing occasionally to skim a page.

"All right," he said presently, his eyes still on the book. "Here's the diagnosis." Lewis glanced up at me. "Shall I read the whole thing to you or do you just want the gist of it?"

"Just the gist, for now."

Lewis closed the book and settled back in his chair. "This man—he was a young guy, twenty-six—was examined by four doctors. They disagreed about some points, but essentially they arrived at the same conclusion. Which was that the guy was psychotic, probably delusional, suffering from schizophrenia, undifferentiated type."

"Schizophrenia, undifferentiated type," I repeated. "That doesn't mean much to me." I paused, biting my lower lip thoughtfully. "Wait a sec. Does that mean that this guy was one of those jokers who sprout twelve different personalities? Like the three faces of Eve or something?"

Lewis smiled tolerantly. "No. The two things really have nothing to do with each other at all. Although a lot of laymen confuse schizophrenia and multiple personality. Multiple personality"—Lewis's voice took on a didactic note here—"is a subtype of what's known as a dissociative reaction. If you want the technical name for it, it's called an altered ego state through hysterical dissociation."

"I thought you told me this wasn't your area of expertise," I said, trying to reproduce everything he'd just said in my notebook.

"It's not," Lewis said cheerfully. "I'm just quoting from a lecture I heard in a seminar I took in abnormal psych my senior year at Stanford." He leaned back a bit further in his chair and put his feet on the desk again, next to the big blue book. "Who you really ought to talk to, Liz, is a good forensic psychiatrist. He or she could tell you a lot more than I can about all this."

"Is that a hint that I'm taking up too much of your time?" I demanded, grinning. "Are you politely asking me to leave?"

"Not at all," he said. "Just trying to be helpful."

"Well, you have been," I said. "Extremely so. Mind if I ask you a few more questions?"

"Go right ahead."

I read over what I'd scribbled in my notebook. A single phrase caught my eye. "This multiple personality business," I began. "Can you tell me more about it?"

"Sure. What do you want to know?" He picked up his coffee cup and drained it.

"First of all," I replied, "if this isn't an asinine question, what causes it?"

Lewis ran a hand back through his curly dark hair before replying. "Well, like a lot of other things, it seems to be traceable to some kind of childhood trauma. Kids who become multiple personalities tend to come from families where one parent is dominant and the other passive. They also tend to be unusually sensitive, so they might feel rejected by either or even both parents. Mostly they've been abused. In a lot of cases, probably sexually abused."

I made a face. "And what's the outcome of that?"

Lewis sighed. "Eventually the kid develops different personalities to handle the different things it experiences."

"OOhhh," I said. "You mean, the kid creates a personality to deal with the violence, and one to deal with love, if it gets any of that, or maybe even one to hide from the abuse?"

"In essence," Lewis replied, "that's it."

"And someone like that," I continued, "could grow up to be a killer like whoever murdered Joan and Sandra?"

"That's entirely possible," Lewis said gravely. "It *has* happened. Not all multiple personalities are homicidal or sexually sadistic, of course, but some of them have been." He leaned a bit toward me. "Remember the Hillside Strangler?"

"Sure."

"Well, at least one psychiatrist diagnosed *him* as a multiple personality."

"Jesus," I murmured. I gave myself a little shake.

"No," Lewis said. "It's not very pleasant, is it?"

I rubbed my forehead. "May I ask you one more question?"

"Certainly."

"With a multiple personality," I said, "does one personality have any idea of the existence of any of the others?"

Lewis squinted thoughtfully. "It can. What happens pretty often is that if there's a violent personality, it knows of the existence of the benign one or ones, but not vice versa."

"I see," I said softly. "So if one of the personalities happens to have those, um, homicidal and sexually sadistic traits and acts on them, then . . ."

"The other personality or personalities wouldn't necessarily be aware of it," Lewis finished for me.

"And there wouldn't be any indication, in the day-to-day actions of this person, that he had this side to him?"

"Nope," Lewis said. "Your friend Bingham was right about that much. This guy could have one personality—his public persona, you could call it—that would strike all his friends and co-workers and such as perfectly pleasant and normal. Guys like this are very often married and have families, and they can be very good fathers and husbands. At least, the part of them that's on view in those circumstances is—well, nobody notices anything even odd or different about them, that's all. The other personalities emerge under stress conditions." Lewis shook his head slowly. "You know, there have been documented cases of individuals having as many as thirty-one distinct personalities. Each one having its own name, its own separate identity."

"My God," I said. "If whoever killed Joan and Sandra *is* one of these characters, no wonder the cops can't catch him."

"Of course not," Lewis agreed. "They're looking for someone who literally doesn't exist most of the time. And with a killer like this, the benign primary personality, the one that most people would identify as the only one, would have no idea that there was a violent alter ego periodically taking over." Lewis waved his left hand. "This guy, whoever he is, the one who murdered those women, probably picks up the newspaper and reads about the killings and is as revolted by them as you or I are."

"A Gemini man," I said, softly.

Lewis looked puzzled. "What?"

I hadn't realized I'd spoken aloud. "Gemini man," I repeated. "Astrology. People born under the sign of Gemini are supposed to have dual personalities. If you believe in that crap."

"Well, I don't really," Lewis laughed. "But it's a good way of describing the kind of guy the police are looking for." His face grew serious. "Hope to hell they find him before he kills another woman."

At that moment, a thin man in plaid wool trousers and a green shirt darted—that's the only way I can describe the movement he made—into the office. I stared at him, startled. He had receding dark hair swept straight back and a narrow, hollow-cheeked face. His expression was irritable.

"Hi, Shelly," Lewis said.

"The monthly report," the man said. "You have it?"

Lewis shook his head. "I passed it on to Carol Gerstein."

"Oh, Jesus," the irritable man replied. "Why'd you do that?"

Lewis looked surprised. "She had some new information she wanted to put in it."

"Oh, for Christ's sake," the man said, exasperated. "Look, we've been late getting that thing submitted for the last three months in a row. Let's not go for four, huh?"

"I'll see what I can do," Lewis said. There was a hint of a smile in his voice.

"Jesus, Jesus," the man said, shaking his head.

"Liz," Lewis said, "this is our director, Sheldon Lederer. Shelly, this is Liz Connors. She's doing a story about Joan Stanley for *Cambridge Monthly*."

"How do you do?" I smiled, holding out my hand.

"Peter," Lederer said. "Call Carol and ask her if she can bring the goddamn thing over here this afternoon, will you?" He turned and left the office. After a second, I let my hand fall to my lap.

Lewis looked at me ruefully. "Sorry about that."

I shook my head. "Don't apologize. I only regret I didn't get a chance to speak with him. He seems charming."

Lewis laughed. "Oh, Shelly's okay. He's a damn good administrator. Good shrink, too. It's just that he needs a vacation. He's been under a hell of a lot of pressure lately. We are so short of money, and he's busting his ass trying to get some funding so we can hold out till the end of the year."

I nodded. "Sure." I shut my notebook and dropped it into my purse. "All the same, I should be getting along." I smiled at Lewis. "Thanks an awful lot."

"You know," he said. "Some of us from the center get together a couple times a week after work for a drink. Maybe you'd like to join us some time." He shrugged diffidently. "You could talk to one of the staff psychiatrists and maybe he or she could fill you in a bit more on this multiple personality business. If you're interested."

I smiled at him. "Well, that's very nice of you. I'll probably take you up on that."

"If you want," he added, "maybe we could get something to eat afterward."

"Oh," I said. I peered at him. Was he asking me for a date? I felt a little flustered, the way I always do when I get an unexpected invitation from a man. Or even an expected one. "Well," I began awkwardly. Perhaps someday, when I'm about fifty-three, I'll acquire the poise to deal gracefully with these situations.

"Well, what?" Lewis said.

"Well, it's very nice of you to ask," I blurted. "But I'm, uh, sort of with someone."

"Oh," Lewis replied. He looked a little confused, as if I'd just said something completely and irrelevantly off the wall, but he was too polite to call my attention to the fact. "Okay."

"Thanks anyway," I said, feeling like The Total Jerk.

Lewis smiled. "Sure." He got up from behind his desk. "Don't forget—if you need any more information for your article . . ."

"I'll be back," I promised. "Thank you again."

"You already have thanked me again," Lewis said. "About three times."

I told him goodbye and shot out of there before I could say anything else dumb.

27

WHEN I GOT home, Jack's car was parked alongside the curb directly in front of my house. Jack himself was in the driver's seat. He didn't notice me coming up the street, I suppose because he had his head bent and was, apparently, gazing intently at the steering wheel.

I walked up to the car and peered in the driver's side window. The steering wheel wasn't what held Jack's attention, but rather a folder full of papers that lay open and resting against it. With my index finger, I tapped on the window. Startled, he glanced up quickly, slapping the folder shut.

"Surprise, surprise," I said.

He smiled at me and rolled down the window. "Hi."

"Been sitting here long?" I inquired. "Thinking deep thoughts?"

"Nope. Just drove up about two seconds ago." He rolled up the window and, tucking the folder underneath his arm, got out of the car. I tilted my face up toward his and he gave me a kiss.

"This is an unexpected pleasure," I said as we walked to the house. "I didn't expect to see you again until Monday."

"What makes you think I'm here to see you?" he asked.

"I suppose," I replied dryly, "that I'm just conceited enough to think that for you, I'm the primary attraction in this neighborhood." I unlocked the front door and pushed it open. "But if you're not here to see me, then why are you here?"

"I want to talk to some of your neighbors."

I paused in the act of stepping into the foyer and threw him a quizzical look over my shoulder. "What for?"

He shrugged. "Just ask them a few questions. There are a couple of things I need to clear up, if I can."

"Oh. Well, is it anything I can help you with?"

"Uh-uh."

"Okay." We went up the stairs. When we reached the second-floor landing, I said to him, "Could I interest you in a cup of coffee or tea? Before you start on your rounds?"

He looked at his watch. "Sure."

"Oh, good." I opened the apartment door, then stepped back and gestured for Jack to precede me.

"What's wrong?" he said.

I gave him a saucer-eyed look of mock astonishment. "Don't you think you oughta go in first and make sure there aren't any bad guys lurking in the bedroom?"

His response was to put his right hand in the center of my back and shove me through the door. "Ladies first," he said. Giggling, I stumbled into the living room. He followed me, shaking his head in portentous resignation.

"Chicken," I said. "And I'm not even armed."

He didn't bother to reply to that. Instead, he dropped the folder on the coffee table and began unbuttoning his sheepskin jacket. He shrugged out of it and tossed it onto the couch.

"Coffee or tea?" I said, removing my own jacket and depositing it next to his.

"Whatever's less trouble," Jack said. "Tea, I guess." He leaned down and retrieved the folder from the coffee table. "Tea okay with you?"

"Dandy," I said. "I've had my ration of lousy coffee for the day."

We went into the kitchen and Jack sat down at the table, setting the folder on the straw place mat before him. I eyed it briefly and covertly, my interest in its contents now considerably piqued. But I made no comment; discretion is my watchword. I went to the sink, filled the kettle with water, set it on the stove, and turned on the gas. I got the teapot from the cupboard, spooned a few tablespoons of loose tea into it, and put it on the counter beside the stove. Then I sat down at the table across from Jack.

"So," I said. "Anything new?"

He gave me another smile. Only this one was less expansive than the first and had a touch of ruefulness in it. "You're referring to the case?"

"What else?"

The smile faded. "I wish I had something to report to you. Been talking to a lot of people, but . . ."

"Nobody's made any startling revelations about Joan or Sandra," I supplied for him.

"That's about where it stands," he agreed.

The kettle made a faint whistling sound. I waited until the whistle had risen to a full-fledged keen. Then I got up and removed the kettle from the stove. As I was pouring the boiling water into the teapot I noticed that Jack had opened the folder and was studying a sheet of lined yellow paper filled with jottings in his own handwriting. Whatever it was, he obviously found it engrossing.

I brought the teapot and two cups to the table. Jack stopped reading, somewhat reluctantly, I thought, and looked up at me.

Curiosity overwhelmed discretion. "What is that, anyway?" I said, nodding at the folder.

"Some notes from a little research I was doing." He closed the folder and pushed it a little to the side.

I poured the tea. "What kind of research?" I asked automatically, handing him a cup. "Or is that a bad question?" I added hastily.

He shook his head. "Not at all." He leaned forward slightly and put his elbows on the table. "I was doing some reading about a business that happened in Indiana a while ago. Three years ago."

I put a spoonful of sugar in my tea and stirred it. "Oh? What business is that?"

He folded his hands together and rested his chin on them. "Ever heard of the Bloomington murders?"

I thought for a moment. The phrase "Bloomington murders" had a vaguely familiar ring, but I couldn't recollect why. "I *think* so," I said slowly. "But I can't remember what they were."

He nodded. "There's no special reason why you should. There was a big uproar at the time about them, though."

I sipped my tea. "What happened?"

"Well, in the course of about three months, seven women in Bloomington got murdered. By the same guy, as far as anybody knows."

"Lovely." I wrinkled my nose in distaste. "Who was it who killed them?"

Jack unclasped his hands and held them up and out, still at chin level. "Good question. There were never any real serious suspects. Cops had their eye on five or six different men at one point or another, but nothing ever panned out." He reached for the small pitcher of milk in the middle of the table.

"I see." I set my cup down and pushed the pitcher over to him. "And after that?"

"Nothing. For all practical purposes, the investigation died after about two years. I mean, it's still officially open, but there's not a hell of a lot left to follow up, at this stage. In fact, there's zip." He put milk in his tea and stirred it slowly.

"Ummm," I said. I cocked my head and gave him a close look. "So what's your interest in the business, then?" I had a feeling I knew, but I wanted to hear him say it.

He was silent for a moment, sucking his upper lip in between his teeth. Then he said, "Far as I can tell, those women got killed the same way Joan and Sandra did. The *exact* same way."

I raised my eyebrows. "And?"

"Well, I thought it was interesting. The similarity."

"Uh-huh," I said. "You thought it was interesting. Nothing else, though."

He looked at me for a moment and then laughed, in a sort of forced and unwilling way.

"Speak," I said. "Give me the specifics."

"Right." He drank some of his tea. "Okay. Seven women, all between the ages of nineteen and thirty-five, all attractive, all with some kind of tie to the academic community—"

"Whoa," I interrupted. "Bloomington's where the main campus of Indiana University is, isn't it?"

"Yup."

I nodded. "Sorry. Go on."

"All right. Each of these women lived alone. Each one was beaten to death, over the head, with some kind of heavy, sharp object, and raped. Whoever did it didn't leave any identifiable prints at the scene. No murder weapon was ever found. There were traces of each victim's blood in the shower or bathtub of her apartment." He broke off the recitation and took another swallow of tea. "Whoever killed them had type A blood."

I was staring at him. "What else?"

He smiled wryly. "What makes you think there's more?"

"Come on, Jack."

"Okay. Each one of those women was known to frequent various bars around the campus. They all seem to have led, uh, very active sex lives."

"My God," I said softly. I finished my tea and, mechanically, refilled my cup.

"Of course," Jack continued. "It could all be a coincidence."

I stirred sugar into my tea. "Do you think it is?"

"I don't know. Those kind of murders of women aren't all that uncommon."

"What kind?"

"Oh, Christ. The kind where a string of women get raped and butchered by some sicko. Offhand I can think of about two dozen other recent cases where the same thing happened. With some minor variations in means and method."

I nodded thoughtfully. "Like what went on here about—when was it? Ten, fifteen years ago? That guy who pretended to be a cop?"

"Oh, yeah." Jack picked up the teapot. "Earl Voltz, his name was."

"Were you in on that investigation?"

He gave a short, sardonic laugh. "Honey, everybody was in on that investigation. Not that it ever led anywhere."

"What do you mean?" I said, startled. "You caught the guy, didn't you?"

"Pure fucking fluke," Jack said, pouring himself more tea. "Voltz ran a red light on Mount Auburn one night and two radio-car guys went after him. They didn't know who the hell they were chasing."

I was fascinated. "What happened?"

Jack shrugged. "Voltz hit a lamppost. Skidded going around a corner. He had a body in the back seat of the car."

"Aughh," I said. "Nice surprise for the two patrol guys."

"Well, they got commendations out of it."

"Where is Voltz now?"

"In Walpole."

"Will he ever get out?"

"He's got six consecutive life sentences to finish serving before he does."

I furrowed my eyebrows. "Why only six? He murdered more girls than that."

"Yeah, but he was only charged with and convicted for six of the killings. The rest, the evidence wasn't strong enough to make cases for."

"But you know he did them."

"Oh, sure."

I got up and carried the empty teapot to the sink. "Did they ever find out what his motive was? Voltz's, I mean?"

Jack shrugged again. "He was put away for the usual thirty days' observation. He wasn't found legally insane. The closest anybody ever got to explaining why he'd killed those girls was that he was punishing them."

I frowned as I scooped the sodden tea leaves from the bottom of the pot and dumped them in the trash. "Punishing them?" I said. "For what?"

"For being whores," Jack said.

I turned sharply from the sink to face him. "Whores?" I repeated. "Who the hell did Voltz think he was? Jack the Ripper? Those girls weren't whores."

"Well, I know that," Jack replied. "But who can tell what kind of associations he was making? Maybe in Voltz's mind, any young, unmarried woman who made herself sexually available to strange men was a whore."

I leaned against the counter, considering his last remark. "Okay," I admitted finally. "I guess there's a certain kind of perverted logic at work there."

"Maybe."

I walked back to the table and sat down at my place. "Do you think whoever killed those women in Indiana and whoever killed Joan and Sandra did it for the same reason as Voltz did? To punish them for, um, screwing around?"

"Could be. Who knows?"

I sighed. "Jack, no one will ever accuse you of jumping to conclusions."

He smiled. "I can't afford to."

"Mmmm. Well—would you like some more tea? Take me two minutes to make it."

"No. No, thanks." He pushed his chair back from the table. "I really have to get moving anyway. I want to try and catch as many of the people in this building as I can this afternoon."

"There aren't that many of us to catch," I replied. "Six and a half, to be precise."

"Oh," Jack said. "The half being, I take it, the Quaalude Kid."

"You got it," I said. "I imagine you'll have a real illuminating chat with him."

"You never know." He picked up the folder and rose from the table.

We walked from the kitchen to the living room. Jack took his coat from the couch and draped it over his arm. Lucy came hustling into the room to say goodbye. Jack leaned down and gave her muzzle a little shake. She pulled free and licked his hand.

"Jack," I said. "This Indiana business."

"Hmmm?"

"You wouldn't be looking into it if you didn't think there were some real possibility of a connection between it and what's happening here, would you? I mean, this research you're doing isn't just for fun, right?"

He smiled faintly. "Hardly."

"But you don't have anything concrete."

"Nope."

I jerked my head at the apartment door. "Are you hoping to get it from my neighbors? Is that what this is about?"

He closed his eyes and shook his head, still smiling. "I never know what I'm looking for," he said, "till after I've found it."

"Words to live by," I said. There was no point in pressing him further. I opened the apartment door. "Well, good luck."

"Thanks." He bent his head and gave me a kiss. I hugged him briefly.

"Have a nice time tonight," I added. He and Sam Flaherty were going to a Celtics game at the Garden. I'd been invited to come along, but I'd passed. I don't have anything against basketball; I just hate sitting in those damn tiers for however many hours. Jack doesn't seem to mind.

176

He left, and I ambled over to the couch and flopped down on it. Lucy hopped up beside me and shoved her head into my lap. I gave her a reflexive scratch behind the ears. The feeling I'd had earlier this afternoon, that there was something awry about the accumulation of facts surrounding the Stanley–Dembkoski case, was with me again. Only this time it was stronger. A sense that somewhere along the line, I'd either forgotten or misinterpreted one key piece of information. Or that a conclusion I'd drawn didn't equate with the evidence available to me.

And . . . was Jack really onto something with this Indiana business? Was he getting nearer to finding the murderer? If so, how would talking yet again to my neighbors help him with that? All of them had maintained, solidly and consistently, that they'd neither heard nor seen anything even remotely suspicious the night of Joan's death. So what, at this point, did they have to offer Jack in the way of useful information? And what could any of them possibly know about a series of unsolved murders committed in Bloomington, Indiana, three years ago?

28

MONDAY MORNING I spent on the telephone with the director of the freshman writing program and the chairman of the English department of Tufts, trying to persuade them to hire me to teach a composition course during the spring. I think I succeeded—not because of my sterling credentials, but because one of their regular people was taking next semester off to have a baby and they needed a substitute for her right quick. I suppose they figured I'd do in a pinch. It's nice to be wanted.

Monday afternoon I had another stimulating tutorial with the goofy kid who wanted to be the next Elvis Costello. In a way, I felt guilty taking payment from his parents. But I consoled myself with the thought that there were far worse ways for them to spend the bread. Like if they gave it to the kid, he'd only blow it on drugs and video arcade games.

We finished up our three-hour session at five-thirty, and five minutes later I was on my way, a substantial check from Mama tucked in my wallet. I was supposed to meet Jack at my place at seven. Instead of going home to get ready, however, I headed for the public library on Pearl Street off Central Square. I wanted to see what literature they had available on the subject of multiple personality. Peter Lewis's speculations on the subject seemed to me to be worth exploring.

I still hadn't come up with any satisfactory, or even half-assed, answers to the questions that had been bothering me since Saturday afternoon.

The branch library on Pearl Street had a surprisingly extensive collection of books on the subject of multiple personality, ranging from the blatantly pop-sensational to the turgidly socioscientific. I spent more time than I really had to spare thumbing through them, a bad habit of mine when I'm around any kind of reading matter. Even what's on the racks at the checkout counter in the supermarket. Finally I selected the three volumes that looked the most useful and brought them to the circulation desk. As he was stamping them with the return date, the librarian asked me if I were doing a term paper for a psych course. I said sort of. He told me he hoped I got a good grade. I thanked him. The last time I'd written a term paper had been in 1971.

It was six-thirty when I left the library, so instead of trekking the two miles back to my place, I walked to Central Square and hailed a cab. That got me home by a quarter to seven. Fifteen minutes to get dressed to go out didn't leave me a margin for dawdling, but if I wasn't ready when Jack arrived, he could make himself a drink and listen to records while I finished putting myself together. Lucy, sensing that I had things to do, insisted on going for a walk. To save time, and in clear defiance of the Cambridge leash laws, I let her out the back door. She scrambled down the steps and galloped across the yard to relieve herself discreetly in a clump of azaleas. My landlord claims that having her around will save him having to buy chemical fertilizer come spring. Maybe.

While Lucy was communing with nature, I went to change. I have two criteria for determining my choice of clothing: mood and occasion. This would be fine if the two ever coincided. Usually they don't. Tonight my mood was daring and expansive, probably the result of the huge tutorial check I had in my wallet. But I didn't know if where Jack was taking me for dinner called for daring. The hell with it. I shucked my jeans and sweater and slipped into the green velvet dress with the high back and long sleeves and nonexistent front. To complete the look I put on some long gold earrings, a Brentano's replication of the baubles Aztec virgins wore for the ceremony where the priests cut out their hearts and offered them to the god of the sun. I stepped back to check myself out in the mirror. Savage pagan barbaric splendor, with just a touch of cool sophistication. Perfect. I repaired my face and hair and went to let Lucy back into the apartment.

Crossing the kitchen, I glanced automatically at the clock and noticed with some surprise that it read seven-fifteen. It was odd for Jack to be late. Or rather, it was odd for him not to have called to tell me he'd be late. I shrugged and went to the freezer to get some ice. I made myself a vodka martini and took it to the living room. I put a Spyro Gyra album on the record player and settled down on the couch to sip and listen.

It was eight o'clock and I had gone from Spyro Gyra to Grover Washington to Bill Evans and a second drink when the doorbell rang. I got up and went over to the intercom by the door, punched the button beneath it, and said into the speaker, "'Bout time, babe."

"Yeah," Jack said. "Sorry."

I pushed the release button for the front door and opened my apartment door. From below, there was a creak and a soft thud and then I heard his footsteps on the stairs. I put my right hand on my hip, grinning a little, poised model-like one foot over the other in the apartment entrance.

He appeared at the top of the stairs. I widened my grin. He didn't return it. So much for pagan barbaric splendor, with just a touch of cool sophistication.

"What's the matter?" I said. "Did the Celts lose Saturday night?"

He shook his head. I peered at him. His face looked a little pale and tight, the skin stretched over the pronounced Indianlike cheekbones. Or maybe it was just the dim hall light. I could feel my grin start to fade a bit.

"What's the matter?" I said.

He looked at me, seemingly vaguely startled by the question. "You're okay," he said. There was a surprised note in his voice to match the expression on his face.

My grin was gone now. "Of course, I'm okay," I said. "Do I look not okay? I'm fine. What the hell's wrong with you?"

He continued gazing at me for another few seconds, and then shook his head. "Let's go inside." Without waiting for my response, he brushed past me into the apartment and walked over to the couch and sat down heavily. Somewhat bemused, I followed him.

"Shut the door," he said.

I closed the apartment door and leaned against it, staring at him. "What's wrong?" I said.

"You didn't watch the news tonight."

"No," I said. "I only got back at a quarter to seven. Why?"

"Come here." He beckoned to me.

Now more than a little concerned, I crossed the room and sat down next to him. This was very un-Jack-like behavior. "What is it?" I put my elbows on my knees and leaned toward him.

"Janice Miller," he said. "The writer for the *Chronicle*." He paused and took a deep breath. "She's dead."

I sat with my chin on my fists for perhaps ten seconds, staring at him. Then I said, "What?" My initial reaction was that I was honestly puzzled. I couldn't grasp what he was saying.

"I tried to call you this afternoon," he said. "You weren't home."

"No," I agreed. "I had a tutorial today, you know, with that jerky kid who wants to be a rock superstar, the little twit who—" I broke off the recital of ephemera. "Janice?" I repeated. "What—Janice is . . . what happened to Janice?"

He reached over and pulled my right fist from beneath my chin. He pried my fingers open and squeezed my hand gently.

"Janice Miller's dead?" I said stupidly. The message still hadn't fully penetrated my brain.

He leaned back and rested his head against the couch cushions. His eyes

180

were focused on the ceiling. In the brighter light of my living room, his face looked if anything even more taut and strained than it had when I'd first seen him.

"Janice?" I repeated. My voice squeaked. "Was it an accident?"

He shook his head and rubbed his free hand over his chin. "No."

I clutched at the hand holding mine. "What, then?"

"She was murdered."

29

I SAT MOTIONLESS, clinging to his hand, staring at him like a stuffed dummy. "God," I breathed finally. "*How?*"

"She didn't show up for work this morning," Jack replied, in a flat, uninflected voice. "She never called in sick or anything. Apparently this was the first time she ever did that, so after a while somebody from the *Chronicle* got worried and tried to call her a couple times. Never got any answer, so finally the managing editor sent a kid over to her place to ring the bell or bang on the door and check if she were, you know, sick or something." He stopped speaking and closed his eyes.

"And?" I probed softly, with a cold expanding certainty that I was going to hear something sickening.

"Messenger didn't have any luck raising her," Jack continued in the same tired monotone. "So—he rousted the building super and talked him into opening the apartment door with his pass key." Jack paused, shook his head slightly, and added, "She was in the bedroom."

"Dead," I interjected, quite unnecessarily.

He nodded. "Christ, the place looked like—I don't know, like a slaughterhouse or something. Jesus, there was blood all over the floor, the walls, the bed . . ."

"Oh, God." My stomach lurched.

"I guess she tried to put up some kind of fight," Jack said. "The night table was on its side and there was a broken lamp on the floor. Probably got knocked off the dresser. Maybe she tried to grab it and hit the guy with it, or throw it at him. Whoever this fucker is, he's as strong as hell."

"How can you tell that?"

"Ah, Jesus. She was beaten to death. By somebody who was very thorough about it. The back of her skull was completely caved in."

Although I was prepared to hear something exactly that horrendous, the preparation didn't lessen the shock. The impact of each word he spoke was the emotional equivalent of being struck by a flying rock. I squeezed my eyes shut and drew in a deep, shuddering breath. Then I said, "Do you have any idea who did it?"

The question was rhetorical, of course; I'd already guessed the answer to it.

Jack made a sound that was a cross between a snort and a laugh. "On the face of it, babe, I would have to say it was the same guy that did in Joan and Sandra."

I could feel my mouth move, but no sound came out of it.

"Except for the mess in the bedroom," Jack went on, "today was like a replay of the other two. Right down to the blood in the tub."

I found my voice. "When did it happen?" I whispered dryly.

Jack shrugged. "Far as the medical examiner could tell then and there, which wasn't much, probably sometime Saturday night, judging by the condition she was in. It was as hot as hell in that apartment, though, which screws up—" he broke off and glanced at me quickly. "Well, skip it. Maybe he'll be able to pin it down better after the autopsy. Saturday night sounds right in terms of what we got in the way of corroborating statements, anyway."

"*What* corroborating statements? My God, are you saying that somebody heard or saw something?"

He made a disgusted face. "Oh, yeah. The jerk in the apartment across the hall from hers said he heard some thumping and crashing coming from her place around eleven-thirty."

"And did he go over to check and see if anything was wrong?" I demanded.

Jack just looked at me.

"No, of course he didn't," I said. "What a ridiculous question. Sorry I asked it."

"Uh-huh."

"Did this idiot say *why* he didn't check up on her?"

"Oh, sure," Jack replied. "He said the noises stopped after a few minutes, so he figured everything was okay." The left corner of Jack's mouth turned down, in a brief, sardonic twitch. "Besides, this character had a woman friend visiting him and he, quote, 'didn't want to wreck the ambience.'"

"Goody for him," I said bitterly. "I hope he had a terrific screw. Did anyone else hear or see anything?"

Jack shook his head. "We haven't caught up with everyone who might have been in the building Saturday night. But no, so far nobody else has come up with anything even remotely useful."

"*Jesus*," I exploded. "So who's the killer, then—the Invisible Man? The Phantom?"

Jack gave me a slight, tired smile. "Seems like it, doesn't it?"

I let go of his hand and let myself sag back against the couch cushions, staring vacantly ahead of me at nothing in particular.

"Was she a good friend of yours?" Jack asked, after a moment.

I shook my head. "No, not a close one. More of an acquaintance, really. We didn't hang out together. I met her a few years ago at a party, and after that we bumped into each other occasionally around town. That sort of thing."

Jack nodded. "Still, I'm sorry."

"I know you are." I reached over and ran my hand down his left forearm.

"You okay?" he said.

"Yeah," I replied. "More or less." I noticed that my hands were trembling minutely. I folded them together in my lap. "Jack?"

"Mmmm?"

"This goddamn thing," I said. "It makes no sense."

"Does it ever?" he replied wearily.

"I'm not talking the philosophy of homicide," I said sharply. "I mean, it makes no sense for Janice to get killed like that." I shook my head violently. "I just don't understand it. How did *she* of all people end up . . ."

He didn't answer immediately. Instead, he got up and paced slowly across the living room, his head bent slightly as if he were in deep thought. He stopped in front of the fireplace and glanced up at me.

"I've been wondering that, too."

"Any ideas?"

"You want what I'm guessing?"

"Yes, of course."

He sighed. "I think it's possible she was using herself as bait."

I frowned at him. "What?"

He stuffed his hands in his pockets and hunched his shoulders slightly. "Bait," he repeated. "Lure."

I shook my head impatiently. "Maybe I'm being dense, but I'm not with you. What are you talking about?"

"You're not being dense. I'm being cryptic." He walked back across the room and sat down next to me. "How much do you know about Janice Miller?"

"Very little. I just told you that, Jack."

He nodded. "Okay, sure. I don't expect you to give me the intimate details of her life. But from a professional standpoint—what was your impression of her? What kind of writer and reporter was she?"

"A good one," I replied promptly. "Very thorough. She triple-checked

184

everything. I remember she once told me she didn't trust anyone's perceptions but her own. And she was very good at putting two and two together." The realization that I was already speaking naturally of Janice in the past tense brought me up short. "God, Jack, you ought to know all this. She was a crime reporter. You've had dealings with her."

"Yeah. All right, what you're saying tallies with my impression. Now tell me this: how far do you think she'd go to get a story or run down a lead or whatever?"

I bit my upper lip, considering. "Well," I said slowly. "She was certainly very tenacious. I mean she'd get hold of something and not let go of it until she'd gotten every drop of material from it she thought she could. I guess I'd have to say she'd go to whatever lengths were necessary."

"Go on," Jack said.

I held up my right index finger, a reflexive schoolmarm gesture. "Okay, a good example," I said. "She told me she once did a series on massage parlors, and as part of her research, she got a job as an attendant at some dump in Kendall Square." I gazed at Jack. "Now how many writers for a small weekly paper would go that far to get a story?"

"Exactly," Jack said.

"So what's that got to do with her getting killed?"

"Think a minute. If she'd work as a massage parlor attendant to get material, then what would she do if she were following up the murders of two girls who were known to frequent local bars and pick up men? Girls who might have been killed by some guy they had a few drinks with and brought home one night?"

"She'd hit the bars and look over the scene. Talk to people, maybe pose as somebody looking for some action," I replied automatically. Then the significance of my own words dawned on me and I added, "Oh, Christ."

"Uh-huh."

"But . . . how—" I fumbled for words. "What—I mean, is that what she did? How can you know that's how she met up with whoever killed her?"

He shrugged. "I don't know that. I'm guessing on the basis of what I know about her reporting habits that that's what might have happened." He turned slightly to face me. His expression was very intense. "Look. Whoever it was killed her, she either brought back to the apartment with her or let in. It was *not* somebody who broke or forced his way into the place. Just like with the other two. As far as I can find out, Janice didn't have any steady boyfriends, no men she was seeing on a regular basis. No rejected lovers, nothing like that. But despite all that, she let a man into her apartment Saturday night and he killed and raped her. And whoever he is, is the same person who murdered Joan Stanley and Sandra Dembkoski. I can't prove that right now, but when the results of the lab tests come back, they're going to say that whoever killed Janice Miller has the same blood type and bite as the one who got the other two."

I ran my hand back through my hair, a nervous gesture. "You're forgetting something, Jack."

He leaned back against the couch cushions. "What's that?"

"I don't want to contradict what you're saying, but—" I paused to collect my thoughts. "Janice Miller was a very shrewd, sharp woman. She was very good at sizing up people. She wouldn't go out looking for a homicidal rapist, find him, and then invite him to come home to bed with her. That's really a dumb thing to do. And Janice was not dumb."

Jack shook his head vigorously. "That's not the point. The point is, she didn't know the guy she brought home was the killer."

"Huh? But—"

"I agree with you that Janice Miller was a shrewd woman," Jack interrupted. "Christ, Joan Stanley was no dummy either. Sandra Dembkoski—well, maybe her selectivity index wasn't all that refined. But all that's irrelevant. What matters is that this son of a bitch, the one who killed those three, whoever he is, he comes on like an Eagle Scout. He could get anyone to trust him. That's how he operates. That's how they all operate. Jesus, how do you think Earl Voltz got those nine girls into his car? It wasn't just the phony badge and gun that did the trick."

I closed my eyes, feeling psychically battered by the force of his argument. The logic was indisputable. "Okay," I said. "So how do you think it went, then?"

"With Janice?" Jack raised his eyebrows. "Maybe she hit a few bars, looked around, got nothing useful, moved on to another place, met this guy, got into a conversation with him, decided she was interested enough to pursue the acquaintance, and let things go on from there. I don't know. I haven't been able to trace her movements Saturday night. If I can, then maybe I'll be able to say better what she had in mind."

"If you can establish that she left a bar with somebody, then you'll know that much, won't you?"

"Well, it'll be a start, anyway."

"Mmmm."

Jack reached into his inside coat pocket and pulled out a pen and a small leatherbound notebook, cracked along the hinge from age and use. He flipped open the notebook, scowled at one of the pages, and scratched his head with the pen. Then he scribbled a few lines on the page, closed the notebook, and slipped it back into his pocket. He rose, buttoning his coat. He was still frowning, in a sort of abstracted way. I was too dispirited to ask why.

"You going back to the station now?" I said.

"Yeah."

"Okay. Call me when you can, huh?"

"Of course." He leaned down and gave me a quick kiss. "I'm sorry as hell about Janice," he added quietly.

I nodded. "Me, too."

30

HE LEFT, AND a kind of clammily palpable silence descended on the apartment. I didn't like it. I glanced at my watch. Only eight-thirty. I had a whole evening ahead of me with which to do whatever I liked. Wonderful. Maybe there was something great I could watch on television. Or I could refinish the rocking chair I'd bought for fifteen bucks in a second-hand furniture store in Somerville. Or I could repair the hem on the quilt on my bed. Defrost the fridge. Trim my bangs. Whoopee. I picked up my drink from the coffee table and sipped it. The ice had melted and it was just vodka-flavored water. Lukewarm, too. I made a face and set the glass back down on the coffee table.

Goddamned if I'd spend this evening alone.

I stood up and kicked off my evening sandals. Then I went to the closet, took out my black riding boots, and tugged them on. Lucy came hustling from the kitchen to see what I was doing. When she saw me reach for my coat, her tail began semaphoring.

"You're out of luck," I said curtly. "Anyway you were just outside an hour ago." I was in no mood to cater to canine whims. I got my handbag from the bedroom and left the apartment before she could start to whine.

Outside it was cold and misty, and there was a fine drizzle falling—total Moulin Rouge weather. The street lights were fuzzy coronas of incandescence. If I passed anyone on the sidewalk, it'd be a dwarf French post-Impressionist in a top hat.

You Toulouse-Lautrec. Me Jane Avril.

There was a restaurant about six blocks away, one of those typical Cambridge soup-salad-quiche-omelet joints with cutesy-pie menus and a clientele to match. No matter. It also had lights and the noise and sense of cheerful heedless life. And I very much needed those things.

The place was jammed, unusual for a Monday evening. The hostess offered me a choice between a twenty-minute wait for a table (which always means a minimum of forty-five minutes) and an immediate seat at the wine and beer bar. I opted for the wine and beer bar. Apparently you could eat there, too, as well as sip new Beaujolais or a California cabernet sauvignon or a Chilean Riesling or Harp lager.

True to its name, the wine and beer bar served only that to drink. Adventurous as always, I ordered a half carafe of the house white. The bartender brought it to me, along with a small wooden bowl of crackers and some Boursin spread. I told him I'd have a spinach salad and an asparagus omelet when the kitchen got around to it.

I drank my wine, and some of the shock and queasy sadness I'd felt since Jack had told me about Janice Miller began to recede. Or maybe it was only that I *still* hadn't fully comprehended what had happened to her. Not that I had any problem visualizing the scene; Jack's description of it had been more than sufficiently explicit for that. The image was something that would stay with me forever, like the memory of what I'd seen the Sunday evening I'd walked into Joan Stanley's apartment.

I finished my first glass of wine and poured myself another.

I glanced around me. All the seats at the bar were taken by people who appeared to be alone. Mostly men, but a few women. I wondered if their reasons for going out tonight by themselves were as dismal as mine. I hoped not. To my left was a bearded young guy in tan sweater and black corduroy jeans who was downing Bass ale as if the U.S. were going to declare an embargo on English beer imports tomorrow. He was staring fixedly at the wine racks behind the bar. To my right was a dandy in a three-piece pale gray suit of European cut, sipping Pouilly-Fuissé. The dandy felt my gaze, looked over at me, and smiled. I quirked my mouth in what I intended as a small polite smile of acknowledgment and went back to my crackers and cheese.

Was it in a place like this that Janice Miller had met the man who'd killed her?

Whoever the bastard was, he had to have been unique. Not your ordinary singles bar beguiler in a Lacoste sweater and Ralph Lauren jeans with a line about the necessity of relating to others on a truly human level. It was perfectly true that I hadn't known Jan well, but I'd known her well enough to be positive that she'd have laughed in the face of anyone like that who'd approached her. Some things you can take to the bank.

Jack was absolutely right. The killer had to have been a man who could disarm even the sharpest, brightest, most self-aware and self-possessed *adult* woman, not just the Sandra Dembkoskis of the world. I *knew* Jan's cynicism about bars and the men who hung out in them looking for available women. She was absolutely the last person to bring home a guy she'd had a drink with and talked to for a half-hour at the most.

189

At that moment, I realized what it was that had been bothering me since Saturday afternoon, the conflict that I'd been unable to identify—let alone resolve.

As far as I knew, Jack was operating on the assumption that Joan Stanley, Sandra Dembkoski, and Janice Miller were probably murdered by a man they met in a bar.

But—and this was the piece of information I'd only now just recalled—it was also very likely that Joan had been killed by someone she'd been expecting to see that Sunday evening, someone she'd opened her door to, someone for whom she'd dressed up in a sexy nightgown. Someone who knew the layout of her apartment well enough to be aware that in her bedroom she had the perfect murder weapon. In other words, A Friend.

So how did that square with the theory of murder committed by a one-night stand?

The bartender brought me my spinach salad. I picked up my fork and poked absently at a slice of mushroom, trying furiously to make some sense of this paradox. I ate a bite of salad, chewing in time to the rhythm of my thoughts.

Wait a minute. The night Jack and I had been in Jim's Place—hadn't Jack asked the bartender if he'd ever seen Joan or Sandra with the same man *more than once*? Sure he had; I'd been too busy adjusting to the notion of Joan Stanley as a barfly to take notice. Presumably Jack had put the same question to the other bartenders he'd spoken to that evening. The purpose of it was suddenly crystal clear to me.

Of course. Joan and Sandra very probably *had* been killed by someone they'd picked up in a joint like Jim's. Only this guy had also been someone with whom they'd had something more than a one-night stand. Say maybe a two- or three-night stand, or even a one-week stand. Time enough, at any rate, for the murderer to get to know a bit about them, a bit about their habits, their routines, the set-up of their apartments. And, most essentially, the opportunity to find out whether they possessed some object—like a cast-iron statue with sharp edges—that might conceivably make a fine, easily accessible murder weapon. That was the key ingredient. The guy needed to have a weapon within reach. After all, you couldn't stroll into a bar looking for a woman to murder and rape with an ax or a hammer tucked into the top of your Frye boots, could you? Somebody might notice and start to wonder about your intentions. Hell, you couldn't walk into a lover's apartment similarly equipped without giving her pause. What would I think if a man I was sleeping with appeared in my bedroom wielding an ax?

190

Okay, then. The murders of Joan and Sandra had been very carefully and methodically planned and carried out by a killer who knew precisely what he was doing every moment. But what about Jan? Could the same be said of what had happened to her? Had she, too, known this man, been his friend or acquaintance, maybe even slept with him on previous occasions? Had she gone out Saturday night looking for a line on a killer, encountered this person she already knew and liked, and invited him to her home, not realizing till the final moments that her quarry and her lover were the same individual?

God . . .

The bartender slid a plateful of omelet in front of me. It looked and smelled wonderful, but I didn't have much appetite. I can't drink and not eat, though, so I dug into the fluffy yellow mass of egg and asparagus with as much enthusiasm as I could muster. I don't recall how it tasted.

I finished as much as I could of the food and pushed the plate to the side. Then I reached for my handbag and took from it a pen and the little notebook I cart everywhere with me. I wanted to write down everything I'd just thought of so that I could keep it all organized.

I had filled half a page with notes when I sensed someone standing beside me. Distracted, I glanced up and to my right. A tall, thin man with swept-back blond hair was leaning against the bar, one foot resting on the brass rail that ran around the perimeter about six inches from the floor. He looked pointedly at my notebook, smiled, and said, "That your dissertation you're working on?"

My dissertation? Jesus, only in Cambridge would you hear an opening line like that. "No," I said, shaking my head and smiling. I went back to writing. When I looked up again, the guy was gone. Probably split to hunt up a chick with an annotated copy of *The Romance of the Rose* and some three-by-five index cards.

There was about one glass of wine left in my carafe. I poured it. Then I jotted down a few last notes in my book and gave the whole thing a quick re-reading. It made sense. I'd have to show it to Jack and ask him what he thought. I closed the notebook and replaced it in my handbag.

I picked up my wine, sipped it, and glanced at my watch. It was ten. I'd give myself another fifteen minutes here and then leave. When I got home, I'd take a nice, hot shower, put on my flannel nightie, make a cup of tea, and climb into bed with a soothing book. I would *not*, under any circumstances, watch the eleven o'clock news.

I looked idly around the restaurant. The room was packed, and so dimly lit beyond the immediate bar area that the people standing even ten feet away were mere silhouettes roaming in an artificial gloaming. The dinner hour was past, and the waitresses were transporting mostly trays of drinks to those at the tables. Over the buzz of conversation, I could hear music. I strained to listen. Sounded like a Quincy Jones tape.

The bearded guy who'd been sitting at my left and putting away Bass Ale had stopped staring at the wine racks behind the bar and was chatting with a slender woman with a pale triangular face, small delicate features, and dark hair in a curly perm. The bearded guy leaned forward and said something to the woman out of the corner of his mouth, like a thirties movie gangster. She burst into laughter and patted him on the shoulder. Her hand slid down his upper arm and lingered there, stroking.

Don't, I wanted to say to her, *don't do it. You don't know who he is. Finish your drink, get your coat, and go home. By yourself.*

Which was just what I should do. I swallowed the last of my wine and signaled to the bartender for the check. He fed it into the register, rang it up, and put it on the counter before me. Seven eighty-nine, tax included. I left a ten-dollar bill on top of it, slid off my bar stool, and got my coat from the rack by the door. As I was on my way out, a short fat guy standing by the exit said to me, "Where'd you leave your horse, honey?" I assumed he was referring to my riding boots. I didn't stop to explain that I wore them because they're the only kind of boot long enough to reach to my knees.

The cold drizzle had stopped, but the fog was, if anything, three times as dense as it had been before. I stood uncertainly in the doorway of the restaurant, debating whether to go back inside and call a cab.

To go six blocks? The hell with it. I'd walked greater distances at later hours in worse weather, a practice of mine that drives Jack nuts. Well, I keep telling him that I haven't been mugged or raped or murdered yet. He's got some real choice comebacks to that.

Other than the sound my boots made hitting the pavement, it was dead quiet on the street. Only an occasional car slid by through the mist. No wandering dogs or cats. No other pedestrians, not even Toulouse-Lautrec. I quickened my stride.

I was home in ten minutes. All the apartments in my building were dark but for mine. I'd left the living room light on, and it was pleasant to walk into warmth and brightness after the murky chill of outdoors. I hung up my coat and kicked off my boots. Then I gave Lucy a pat and went into the bedroom to remove my dress. The dog trailed me. I had just finished peeling off my panty hose when she made a small yipping noise and began cavorting around by the bedroom door. I stopped what I was doing and glared at her.

"Don't tell me," I said wearily. "You want to go outside, right?"

She sat back on her haunches and thumped her tail against the rug, a big grin stretching her silly, furry face.

"I don't know why the hell you have to wait till I'm undressed to decide that," I grumbled. I got my robe from the closet, shrugged into it, and tied the belt around my waist. "All right, come on," I said, and walked to the kitchen. She raced ahead of me, tail wagging. I opened the back door and let her out. She was used to going down the steps from my back porch to the yard by herself. "You be right back here in five minutes," I hissed after her. "Or else." I left the door ajar about an inch so she could nose her way inside when she returned, and went to the bathroom to brush my teeth.

I was winding my hair into a sloppy chignon so it wouldn't get soaked in the shower when I heard a noise in the kitchen. "That was quick," I called. I took the last bobby pin from the counter and jabbed it into the knot of hair.

"Don't like it much outside when the weather's lousy, do you?" I remarked, as I walked down the little hall connecting the bathroom and the kitchen.

I stopped dead in the entrance to the kitchen, staring. There was someone in the room, and it wasn't the dog. It was a tall man in jeans and a brown nylon jacket open over a gray sweatshirt. A good-looking man with curly dark hair and hazel eyes. He wasn't a stranger. In fact, I'd met him three times before tonight. He'd even been in my apartment one of those times, the Sunday after Joan Stanley had died.

It was Peter Lewis.

31

ODDLY, I WASN'T especially frightened. Not at first, anyway. But I was very, very, very startled. So I said the first thing that popped into my head.

"My God, you nearly gave me a coronary." I sagged against the doorjamb, my right hand pressed to my chest.

"Sorry," Lewis said. "Didn't mean to make you jump." His voice sounded a little husky, almost as if he were coming down with a cold. He smiled at me with sincere rueful apology.

"Well, you did," I replied. "God!" The upheaval in my chest made me cough. I hunched over slightly, my shoulders shaking.

"Take a deep breath," Lewis suggested.

I did do, and the pounding of my heart subsided a bit. I straightened up slowly.

"That's better," Lewis said.

My initial shock at finding him in my kitchen was succumbing to an overwhelming bewilderment. I drew another fortifying breath, and asked the question I should have asked immediately. "What are you doing here?"

He only shrugged, smiling.

I peered at him uncomprehendingly for a few seconds and then said, "That's not an answer. What do you want?"

Still no reply. I glanced quickly at the kitchen door. It was shut tight, and the bolt had been slid home. That must have been the noise I'd heard while I was in the bathroom. I looked back at Lewis. He was standing motionless, watching me very closely. The first little curl of anxiety began to snake its way up my spine. What in God's name was going on here? And what in hell did Lewis think he was doing? Was he drunk? Drugged? If so, he had none of the usual symptoms of either condition. His speech was clear, despite the slight alteration in the pitch of his voice. He wasn't babbling incoherencies. His eyes weren't glazed or unfocused. He wasn't having any trouble holding himself upright.

Far as I could tell, the man was as sober as a Baptist deacon on Easter morning. The realization merely increased my unease.

194

"I think you ought to leave now," I said, making an effort to keep my voice calm and firm.

"Leave?" His voice was light, almost teasing. "Why?"

I stared at him. "Because I'm telling you to," I said sharply.

He shook his head, grinning, and leaned against the counter. "I just got here. Why do you want to throw me out?"

"Look," I said. "A gag's a gag, okay? I don't know what kind of dumb stunt you think you're pulling, but if you don't get out of here right now . . ." I let the threat hang unfinished in the quiet kitchen air.

"What are you so uptight about?" he said. "It's not like I'm a total stranger or anything. You've been to see me. I came to see you. What's the big deal?"

At that, I felt a surge of anger, compounding the apprehension and confusion. I ignored the question. "Out," I said, jerking my head at the kitchen door. "*Now.*"

"Come on," he said. "Talk to me for a while." He pushed himself away from the counter and took a step toward me. Automatically, I retreated a pace.

"Hey, relax," he said. He held out a hand, as if to draw me to his presence. I flattened myself against the wall behind me and crossed my arms over my chest, the instinctive gesture of self-protection.

"No," I said. "Get out."

"I'm not leaving," he replied gently.

"Yeah, you are," I snapped.

Again, he shook his head.

It was at that moment that I felt the first flicker of real fear. I tried to force my way through it. There were decisions I had to make, and I couldn't afford to panic. I closed my eyes. Be cool, I told myself. Pretend it's okay. Pretend what's happening now makes perfect sense. Talk your way out of this, whatever this is. You can do that much. You're good with words.

"I was watching you tonight," Lewis said abruptly.

My eyes flew open. "*What?*"

"In the bar," Lewis answered. "I saw you come in and I saw you leave. I watched you the whole time you were there." He paused a moment and then added, "You didn't see me, though." He sounded almost regretful.

Stunned into speechlessness, I could only stare at him.

"You looked nice," he continued. "I like that dress you were wearing." He let his gaze fall to my feet and then travel upward, slowly. "You look nice now, too." He frowned slightly. "You should take down your hair, though. I like it better when it's loose."

My throat felt as if a golf ball were lodged in it. I swallowed with some difficulty and some pain. "What do you want?" I said.

"I *told* you," he replied. "I just want to talk to you. Be with you for a while." His voice was soft, reassuring. "Come on. Sit down." He gestured at the kitchen table.

I hugged my arms more tightly across my chest. "No."

He sighed. "Now stop being silly. What's the matter with you, anyway? All I want to do is sit down and talk. Come on."

In that instant, I made up my mind what I was going to do. "No," I said, with a firm assurance I didn't feel. "I want you to leave. Now." I took one cautious step forward.

Lewis didn't move, but his facial expression altered subtly, from patience to wariness. My sudden display of assertiveness must have caught him off guard.

"Right," I said. "I'm going into the other room. If you're not out of here in five seconds, I'm calling the police."

He didn't say anything.

I waited a moment and then shrugged. "If that's the way you want it," I said in tones of contrived casualness. I had to go past him to get to the living room and the phone and the front door. I bit my lip nervously. Then, keeping my eyes forward, I walked out of the kitchen and into the hall. I could feel the weight of Lewis's gaze on me as I approached him. Keep going, I told myself. Don't run, don't slow down, don't hesitate. Just walk past him. Don't even look at him.

It wasn't until I'd reached the entrance to the next room that he made his move. I felt a sudden unbelievably sharp pain in the back of my head and then I was being dragged backward. I staggered and nearly fell. Lewis caught me around the waist with his left arm and pulled me against him, so tightly that I could feel the pressure of his belt buckle and jacket zipper through my quilted robe. His right hand was twined in my hair. He bent his head so that his mouth was only an inch or so away from my ear. "I told you I'm not leaving," he whispered. He twisted the knot of hair at the back of my head as if to emphasize the point. My scalp felt as if it were on fire.

"Am I getting through to you?" he said.

I nodded, acknowledging not only the question but a sick sense of my own helplessness.

"Good," he said. He released me. I leaned against the kitchen table and rubbed the back of my head, blinking to clear away the tears of pain that had welled up in my eyes.

"And take those fucking pins out of your hair," Lewis added.

Most of them had been yanked out of place when he'd grabbed me. Obedient as a zombie, I removed the remaining two and my hair fell to my shoulders.

"That's better," Lewis said. He stared at me for a moment and his face softened. "I'm sorry I had to hurt you," he said. "But if you try to walk away from me again, I'll do the same thing. I don't want to, but if you force me to, I will. And it might be worse the next time."

I raised a hand in a gesture of concession, too enervated by shock and fright to do anything else. Besides, I couldn't see an alternative.

"I don't know why you're so afraid of me," Lewis said. "I just want to talk to you. That's all." He gave me a look that was very close to pleading.

I drew a long, tremulous breath. "Okay," I said. "I'll talk to you."

"Good." His reply was brisk, cheerful. I wondered if he'd rub his hands together.

"Let's sit down," Lewis said. He pulled out the kitchen table chair nearest where I was standing, then took me by the shoulders and pressed me down gently into the seat. He lowered himself into the chair to my left. It was the one Jack habitually used.

We looked at each other.

"So," Lewis said. "Did you have a nice time tonight? At that bar?"

I may have been mistaken, but it seemed he placed some emphasis on the last word. I nodded briefly, hoping I was making the proper response to the question.

"That's good," Lewis replied. He put his right foot on the table and tilted back his chair. "I had a nice time, too." He grinned, "Watching you."

I was silent.

"You go out a lot by yourself?" he asked. "At night?"

I eyed him carefully. There was no way I could even begin to guess where this was leading, or much more importantly, what my role was supposed to be. "Sometimes," I said carefully.

He nodded thoughtfully. "No reason why you shouldn't. Still . . ." His voice trailed off and he arched a speculative eyebrow at me. "Remember the last time you came to the counseling center?"

"I remember."

"I asked you to have dinner with me. You told me you couldn't because you were already seeing somebody else."

"That's true," I said. "I am."

197

"Yeah. So this guy must be somebody you're pretty serious about, huh?"

"Yes."

Lewis leaned forward slightly and gave me a sharp, probing look. "Then where was he tonight? This guy you're so tight with?"

I put my hands in my bathrobe pockets. "He had to work."

"Oh," Lewis said. He scowled, not angrily but abstractedly, as if trying to reconcile two patently incompatible ideas. "So you went out by yourself."

"Yes."

"And you had a nice time."

"It was all right."

"I bet it was." Lewis let himself relax back into his seat. The scowl faded from his face and, slowly, he began to smile. "I bet it was," he repeated. Something about the tone of his voice made the skin on the back of my neck tighten.

"I saw you talking to some guy," Lewis said. "And I saw you looking around, too, at the others in there."

I shrugged, hoping the gesture would be interpreted as noncommital.

"You fucking slut bitch," Lewis said calmly.

I recoiled as if he had punched me, feeling my eyes widen with shock.

"Jesus." Lewis shook his head. "You really are something else, you know that?" He took his foot from the table and set it on the floor with a heavy solid thump, as if he were crushing some insect scuttling along the tiles, visible only to him. "What the hell's the matter with you? You can't spend one night alone? You have to go out looking for it?"

"I don't know what you mean," I said falteringly.

"Shit," Lewis said. "The fuck you don't." His face had flushed an ugly, congested red. I could hear him breathing, too, and see his chest rise and fall with each inhalation and exhalation.

"I thought maybe you were different," Lewis continued. "Not like those other sluts. But you aren't any different from them, are you? I saw that tonight, when you were talking to that man. You're just like the rest. Just a fucking tramp."

"No," I said, barely able to enunciate the single syllable.

"Yes," Lewis said. In a sudden swift movement he lunged across the table and grabbed my face. "I know you now. You fooled me at first, yeah, I'll give you that. But now I know you, you showed me what you are tonight." His fingers dug into my cheeks. "You're evil, you know that, you're filth, you're dirt."

I shivered uncontrollably and squeezed my eyes shut, so that I wouldn't have to look at him. I felt dizzy and sick, my mind a gray, buzzing blank. Nothing was real except the dark, convoluted, incomprehensible menace that had invaded this room. That and the fear.

As suddenly as he had taken hold of it, Lewis let go of my face. "Aaaahhh," he exclaimed, his voice vibrating with disgust. "What's the point? You don't understand."

I opened my eyes. He had flung himself back in his seat and was gazing at me with sulky fury, like a large, petulant child. I raised both hands to my face and massaged my cheeks, still feeling there the pressure of his fingers. I recalled, dimly, that the last time I'd been to talk to Lewis at the counseling center, I had noticed that he had the look of someone of enormous physical strength. I hadn't been mistaken in that perception. And when he grabbed me as I tried to leave the kitchen . . . I shivered again and let my hands fall to my lap.

Jesus God, what was I going to do? How was I going to get out of this? There was absolutely no chance of my overpowering Lewis. And very little of even fighting him off. Unless I could maneuver him into a position where I could—do what? Kick him in the groin, maybe? Wasn't that one of the tactics recommended for a woman being attacked by a man?

But suppose I missed? Or I hit him, but not hard enough to disable him even temporarily? Chances were that was exactly what would happen. I had no experience with this sort of thing, no training in self-defense. I'd never in my life been physically threatened. Despite the events of the past few weeks, violence was still mostly an abstraction to me, something Jack dealt with and I heard about at second hand. The last time I could remember hitting anyone was when, at the age of fourteen, I'd slapped my younger sister for spilling mustard on my favorite sweater. Great preparation for confronting the present situation.

I'd infuriated Lewis merely by trying to walk away from him. How, then, would he react if I tried to punch or kick him?

It was, I realized in that moment, not just terrifying to be so absolutely in someone else's control, but sickening, enraging. Disgusting. A kind of violation—no, a *statement* on the part of the one doing the controlling that you were nothing, certainly not human, and probably less than an animal. That you only existed at the pleasure of the controller's whim.

Okay, I told myself. Don't think about it. If you do, you'll get hysterical. What the hell does it matter how you feel about what's happening now? You can analyze your feelings all you want, later. Forget everything except how you're going to get out of this. Concentrate on that.

"You don't understand," Lewis repeated.

He was right; I didn't, but I was beginning to, and maybe that was the worst part.

I folded my hands and stared at him, trying to be cool and rational.

Out of the corner of my eye, I saw Lewis move. Reflexively, I tensed. He shifted slightly in his chair and stretched out his legs, crossing them at the ankles. I raised my head and peered at him. The flush had died out of his face, but there was a residue of anger there, and something else that was oddly like determination. As if he'd arrived at a decision and was preparing himself to carry it out. Seeing him thus, I could remember a time when I'd found that face attractive, compelling even. Well, it was still compelling. But for a much different reason.

His voice broke in on my thoughts. "What you did tonight was bad. Wrong."

Oh, God. Were we still on that? I shook my head, a defeated gesture of confusion and negation. What answer could I give him? What question was he asking? Was he even asking a question?

"Look," I said wearily. "I wish you'd tell me what it is you want. I went out by myself tonight to have dinner. That's all."

"No," he insisted. "That wasn't all." He tilted his head and gave me a look as intense and as focused as a beam of light. "You know it and I know it, so why don't you knock off the bullshit?" He paused and then added flatly, "You were out tonight to get laid, honey."

I didn't say anything.

"So how come you came home alone, so early?" he continued. A sly challenging note crept into his voice. "What happened? Didn't you see anything you liked?"

I opened my mouth to reply and then shut it. Was there any point in arguing with him?

He studied me for a moment and then shrugged negligently. "Doesn't matter," he said. "I'm still going to make you pay for what you did."

Pay?

There was a sensation inside my head like what happens to a burning lightbulb when you throw water on it. I made a fist and slammed it on the table top. "I didn't *do* anything," I nearly screamed. "What in God's name is so wrong? Will you tell me that? What do I have to pay for? I did nothing, I—"

"You're a whore is what you are," he interrupted. His face was as flat and tight as his voice. "That's what you have to goddamned pay for."

I shook my head again, frantically this time, denying—what? The accusation? The threat? Or just the reality of what was happening in this room?

Lewis's eyes raked my face, as if searching it for signs of comprehension. "Christ," he said. "You really don't understand, do you?"

"No," I said, almost choking on my own rage and terror. "No."

He gave a brief laugh that was virtually indistinguishable from a snort. "No reason you should," he said. "The others didn't."

I inhaled sharply. "The others?" I repeated. "What others? What the hell are you talking about?"

I knew, then, of course, but I had to pretend I didn't.

He gazed at me as if I were preternaturally stupid. "All those other fucking sluts," he replied, with considerable emphasis and impatience. "They didn't think there was anything wrong with what they were doing, either." He stopped speaking for a moment, looking thoughtful. "Of course," he added. "I didn't tell them the way I'm telling you. Except for the last one. Her I told." He gave another one of those abbreviated nasty snickers. "She wasn't very receptive to the idea, either. Dumb bitch." He made a gesture with his right hand as if brushing away a gnat. "Fucking snoop reporter. Well, she paid all the same."

I stared at him, barely breathing, the phrase "fucking snoop reporter" flashing on and off in my brain like a neon sign.

"Put up a hell of a fight, though," Lewis conceded, with a sort of reluctant admiration. "But then, she knew what I was going to do. The others didn't."

I licked my lips. "What did you do?" If I didn't hear him say it, I would never believe it. "What did you do?"

"Jesus Christ," Lewis said, exasperated. "What the fuck do you think I did? I killed her. I killed all of them. Fucking cunts didn't deserve to live."

There was a roaring in my ears and my heart began to pound in slow, shaking thuds. The walls of the kitchen seemed to belly inward toward me.

Lewis's voice came to me as if from the opposite end of a long, narrow tunnel. "The bitch from the paper and that stupid little blond lush were easy. Didn't bother me at all, wasting them."

I felt as if I were suffocating, as if I would never again be able to breathe sufficient oxygen to sustain consciousness or even life.

"The one before them was harder for me," Lewis continued, his eyes liquid and shimmering with some unfathomable emotion. "I liked her. We were friends. I thought she was beautiful. We made love a couple times, even. I thought maybe we . . ." He broke off and gave his head a single shake, as if rejecting whatever memory or recollected hope had invaded his mind. "But then I found out what she was, and—I had to stop her, you know? I couldn't let her go on that way. I thought I was the only one she . . . but she was with other men. Too many men." He paused a few seconds. When he spoke again, his voice was vibrating with incredulity and outrage. "She *told* me about them, for Christ's sake. Some professor and . . . and she was even supposed to be engaged to one of them. *Jesus*."

I hunched over, hugging myself. "Joan," I said faintly. "You mean Joan. You killed Joan."

He nodded.

"*Why?*" The question burst out of me like the contents of a lanced boil, something I couldn't contain. "Why did you do that? How could you do that? Peter, you—"

His body jerked as if a charge of electricity had passed through it. I pushed back in my chair, putting as much distance between us as I could.

"What did you call me?" he asked softly.

I stared at him wordlessly.

"Peter," he said. "You called me Peter, didn't you?"

When I didn't reply, he reached across the table and grabbed my face, as he'd done earlier when I'd refused to acknowledge my sluthood. He squeezed my jaw until I could feel my lips purse up like a fish's.

"Answer me," he said.

"Yes," I said, after a moment. It came out as "yesh."

He slapped me. "Call me that again, and I'll kill you right here, now, this minute."

"I'm sorry," I whispered, trying to be placating. "I thought Peter was your name."

"It's not my name," he said. "It's that fucking wimp's name. *Peter*." He spat out the "Peter" as if it were some incredibly foul-tasting substance that had burned his tongue. "Stupid asshole."

I felt as if I had been administered, against my knowledge and consent, a dose of the world's most powerful hallucinogen. "You're not Peter?"

"No, I'm not Peter," he snapped, in a falsetto obviously intended to mimic my own voice.

I swallowed. "Who are you then?"

He gave me a look that was part pity and part contempt for my slowness. "I'm Tom. Call me Tom. That's who I am. Tom Lawrence."

32

SUDDENLY EVERYTHING MADE sense. More or less.

All the questions I'd had about what had happened over the past few weeks had been answered by the person sitting not three feet away from me. The stranger sitting not three feet away from me.

I peered at him. Physically, it was Peter Lewis. No doubt about that. The face, the coloring, the build, were identical to the face and the coloring and the build of the man I'd talked and laughed with on three occasions before tonight. But there were noticeable differences, too, now that I was looking for them. First, of course, the appalling crudeness of his language. And the peculiar alteration of his voice, the huskiness I'd noticed earlier. I'd attributed it to an incipient cold.

Was it not, in fact, that, but merely the normal speaking voice of this new person? This Tom Lawrence creature?

With a start, I realized that my mind was functioning rationally again, sorting out data and putting it together. How bizarre. I was in the worst danger of my life, yet here I was, studying the source of that danger as if it were the trick question on the final exam in History 241.

Maybe it was only that now I knew what I was up against. Maybe when I got used to that, the fear would return.

The thing across the table from me, whatever it was calling itself, whoever it was, had murdered and raped three women. And it had told me that I was number four on its list. I had no reason to believe it wouldn't try to do what it had promised. The rage within the thing was emanant, radiant like body heat.

It spoke then, and its voice echoed in the otherwise silent kitchen. "I hate that miserable fucker."

I held myself perfectly still, watching it. It had turned its face away from me and was gazing at the blank white wall behind the table. What it saw there, I had no way of knowing. Nor any desire to know.

"Stupid shit," it continued. "Hate him. He wants to *help* people. Be good. How the fuck can you help a bunch of retards and mentals and fuckheads? Asshole."

"Peter," I said, softly, tentatively. "You're talking about Peter, aren't you?"

The thing transferred its gaze from the wall to me. "I hate him," it repeated.

The thought occurred to me that if I could keep the thing talking about its loathing of Peter, I might be able to distract it enough so that it would forget why it had followed me home this evening. For a while, anyway.

Yeah. Then what?

"Is it just because he's good that you hate him?" I asked, in the same lullaby tones.

The thing stirred a little in its chair. "He won't let me out. He tries to keep me inside."

"Inside?"

"Inside him."

"He knows about you then?" I said. "He knows who you are?"

"No," the thing replied, its voice heavy with disgust. "He's too fucking stupid."

"Oh," I said. I paused for a moment, thinking up a next question. "If he doesn't know about you, how does he keep you—inside?"

The thing made an impatient movement with its shoulders. "He just does, that's all."

"But you *do* get out."

"Oh, yeah." The thing grinned, a flash of white in the thin, dark face. "I get out. Yeah."

Bad question. I sought to recoup. But what the hell else could I ask it that wouldn't inevitably lead back to its reason for coming here tonight?

"Is there anyone else you hate as much as you hate Peter?" I said. I hoped the desperation in my voice wouldn't be obvious. It might have the same effect on the thing as blood in the water does on sharks. I tried to steady my voice. "Who else do you hate that much?"

The thing furrowed its brow, as if thinking hard. I waited, not taking my eyes off it.

"Aaahh," it said finally. "I hate—" It broke off speaking and grimaced, almost as if in pain.

"Who?" I prodded gently.

"Everybody," it said, and there was an anguish in that single word that went beyond any expression of grief or hurt that I'd ever before heard.

"You hate everybody," I said.

It closed its eyes and nodded, just once, its head bent.

"That's so sad," I said, as calmly as I could. "Why do you hate everybody? Isn't there anyone you like? Anyone at all? There must be."

It shook its head.

"That's awful," I continued, as if I were commiserating with a six-year-old over the loss of a puppy. "I'm so sorry. Wasn't anyone ever nice to you? What about your family?" I couldn't believe I was being this cool, this reasonable. Why wasn't I having hysterics? "What about your family? Like, your parents. Your father or your mother or—"

Its head snapped up. "I hate her."

I blinked and drew a deep breath. "Who?"

"Mother." The loathing in the voice was nearly physical in its intensity.

"Your mother," I said, as steadily as I could in the face of such violent emotion. "You hate your mother."

"Bitch," it said. "Mother. Bitch. Hate her. *Hate* her."

"Why?" I said. "Why do you hate her?"

"Hurt—me." The thing's voice was slow and dragging, like the sound of a record played at insufficient speed.

"She hurt you," I echoed.

"Hurt me," it repeated. "Hurt."

Christ, where did I go from here? Did it matter?

"What did you do?" I babbled. "When she hurt you?"

It didn't reply for a moment. When it did, its voice was even thicker. "Went—away."

I leaned forward a little and stared at it. "You went away?"

"Went away."

"Where?"

"Inside."

"Inside where?"

"Inside."

I sat back, staring at it. The thing was slouched in its chair, its body slack, its face vacant.

"How did she hurt you?" I asked.

"Hurt me. *Hit* me."

I nodded, with no idea of what I was agreeing with.

"Went away," it said.

"I know," I said. "You went away."

"*No*," it said. "*She* did. Went away. Left."

"Oh," I said quietly.

"Hate her." The thing moved a little in its seat, as if seeking a more comfortable position. "Hate everybody." It sighed deeply. "Hate Peter." It stopped speaking, and, slowly, a grin began to crack its face. "Took care of him, though. Peter."

"Oh?" I repeated, in a neutral tone. "You did?"

"Dumb asshole," the thing said. "Took care of him. Told him to kill those girls. He did, too."

I tensed. "I thought *you* did that. To punish them."

The thing laughed, a dry creaky sound. "Used him. Made him do it."

"Why?" I said breathlessly.

"Mother."

I let a few seconds pass. Then I said, "You made Peter kill them"—I couldn't bring myself to say anything about rape—"because of your mother?"

It nodded.

"Why?" I asked again, my voice nearly inaudible.

"Hurt," it said. "Mother. Joan. Went away. Whore."

Comprehension hit me like a sledgehammer.

"Why did your mother go away?" I said.

The thing hesitated. "Man," it said, in tones so soft I could barely catch that lone syllable.

"Your mother went away with a man? She left you?"

"Yes. Hurt."

"What about your father?"

"No father."

I sagged back in my chair, my hands cupped around my elbows. I felt as if I were a millennium old and a century past dying.

The thing was motionless in its chair, like a lizard on a sun-baked rock.

So what did I do now, now that I knew all that there was to know? Get up and walk away? Ask more questions? Play shrink?

There was a slight scratching noise at the back door. I jumped, and so did the thing. Its head whipped around and it stared at the door. Despite its air of somnolence, its nerves must have been stretched as tightly as were mine.

"What's that?" the thing demanded.

The scratching sounded again, this time accompanied by a whine. I recognized it, and had a wild impulse to laugh.

"My dog," I explained. "I think she wants to be let in."

"Oh, yeah," the thing said. It relaxed back into its chair. "That brown mutt I saw the last time I was here."

I nodded, not really paying attention. Suddenly I could see a way out of

206

this. I could practically hear the relays in my brain clicking as they processed the plan. What I had to do was persuade the thing to let me open the kitchen door. Once Lucy got inside . . . she was a mild little creature, of course, timid with strangers. But like all dogs, she could sense danger in the air like a bad smell. And she was protective of me, her person. If the thing made any sort of threatening move at me, she'd be on it in a second. For her size, she was a strong, heavily muscled animal. And I had seen those fangs and jaws demolish a beef bone two inches in diameter.

The scratching noise was repeated, more loudly and insistently.

Go ahead, I thought, what do you have to lose by it?

"I think she really wants to come in," I said. I hesitated a beat. "May I open the door?"

The thing didn't answer.

I waited another moment, letting the silence between us lengthen. Then I got up, slowly, gathering the folds of my robe around me. I kept my eyes on the thing's face. It was perfectly still, watching me. I took a cautious step forward.

"Sit down," it said.

I froze in the act of sliding one foot in front of the other.

"I said, sit down, goddammit." The thing half rose from its chair, bending toward me. The flush was rising again in its face, an angry spreading stain beneath the skin.

Like an actor in a movie being shown in reverse, I retraced the step and a half I had taken and lowered myself into my chair.

"You must think I'm an imbecile," the thing said.

I shook my head in instinctive denial, mentally cursing myself for what I'd just done. It *had* been a stupid idea. Ridiculous. Had I actually imagined that the thing would let me walk to the door and open it and let the dog in—or, for all it knew, myself out? To go running down the stairs screaming for help?

It shot me a look that was part disbelief and part contempt. "Jesus, you really thought I didn't know what you were trying to do, did you?"

"No," I said softly. "I mean, I wasn't trying to fool you." How hollow, how patently false the words sounded.

It got up, walked around the table to where I was sitting, and hit me. The blow nearly knocked me out of my chair.

"I told you what would happen if you tried to walk away from me again," it said. It struck me once more, a backhanded swipe across the right side of the face, and this time I *did* fall out of the chair. I hit the wall to my left, slid down it, and collapsed on the floor, half-sitting, half-crouching. My skull felt as if it were vibrating.

The thing knelt down beside me, put its hand beneath my chin, and yanked up my head. It lowered its face to within three or four inches of mine.

"I'm going to fucking kill you," it said. "Right now."

I jerked my chin out of its hand and threw myself to the side, in the direction of the entrance to the other room. I rolled over once, scrambled to my knees, and pushed myself up and forward like a runner taking off from the starting line. My right foot caught in the hem of my robe and I tripped as I was going through the doorway. I stumbled forward about three paces into the bedroom and then fell, face first, across the bed. Almost as soon as I hit it I was flipping over onto my back. I was bouncing up, shoving myself with my elbows off the bed, when the thing was through the doorway and on me.

The weight and impact of its body hitting mine knocked all the air out of me. For a moment I was completely incapacitated, feeling as if I'd been steamrolled. The thing raised itself slightly, slid a hand between us, and tugged at the knot in the belt of my robe. I placed the heels of my hands against its shoulders and pushed as hard as I could, practically grunting with the effort. It didn't budge. My legs were pinned beneath its, so I couldn't kick. I tried to twist the upper half of my body to the side. With its free hand, the thing pushed me back onto the mattress. I felt the knot in my belt loosen and give and my robe fall open.

The thing put its hand on me, and in that instant, I knew something I'd never before experienced. The urge to kill.

Nobody does this to me.

I made a fist and drove it with all the strength I possessed straight into the thing's throat, right at the protrusion of the Adam's apple.

The thing's eyes bulged and it made a noise that was halfway between a squawk and a gag. It reared up and back, swaying, and then toppled to the left, collapsing on the pillows. I slid out from beneath it, rolled over twice, and hit the floor with a thud.

I was up as soon as I landed, tying my robe close around me.

The thing struggled to its knees, one hand to its throat, gasping for air. It turned its head and stared at me, chest heaving. Its eyes were luminous with hatred. Slowly, painfully, it rose from the bed.

I dashed into the living room and looked around wildly, seeking anything that might serve as a weapon.

Weapon? God almighty. The kitchen was full of them. Knives of all shapes and sizes. Too bad I wasn't near the kitchen. The thing was near it, though. All it had to do was go in there and pluck something sharp out of the dish drainer or cutlery drawer.

I could hear its footsteps approaching. I spun around in a frenzy, searching. Out of the corner of my eye I saw the log basket to the left of the fireplace. I ran over to it. There was a single log at the bottom of the basket, part of a branch actually, maybe two feet long and three inches in diameter. I grabbed it and raised it over my head just as the thing came through the living room entrance.

"You bitch," it croaked. "I'm gonna fuckin' rip you to pieces."

I braced myself, feet apart. "Like hell you are," I said.

It came at me in a rush. When it was about a yard away, I brought the log down on its head as hard as I could, as if I were driving home a railroad spike.

For maybe five seconds the thing stood before me, motionless, its face frozen with shock and pain. Then it wavered and, slowly, sank into a huddle at my feet. I stared down at it, panting, and raised the log over my head, preparing to bring the wood crashing down yet again. And again. And as many times as might be necessary.

The thing moaned and gave a kind of convulsive shudder. I kicked it in the ribs. It stretched out slowly, tried to rise, and fell back on the floor.

"All right now, you son of a bitch," I whispered. "That one was for me. The next ones are for Joan, and for Sandy, and for Janice." My hand tightened on the piece of wood.

The thing on the floor mumbled something.

"What?" I said.

Its voice was a little clearer this time. "Hurt."

"Yeah," I said. "But not nearly as bad as it's going to."

The thing rolled over onto its side and wrapped its arms around its head. It shoulders hunched. Its legs moved so that the thighs were drawn upward to the chest.

A few seconds went by before I realized that it was assuming the fetal position.

"Hurt," it said. "Hurt. Hurt."

I stared down at the thing with a kind of sickened fascination.

"Hurt," it repeated, in a high, childish voice. "No more. Don't hurt. Didn't do nothing bad. Please don't hurt." It stopped speaking and twitched.

I let my arm fall to my side. I dropped the log. It fell to the floor and rolled harmlessly away in the direction of the couch.

"Mommy," the thing said, "don't hurt no more." It looked up at me, its face a mask of supplication. I turned my head away quickly, so that I wouldn't have to see the expression in those eyes.

"No," I said, softly, tiredly. "I won't hurt you. Don't worry."

The thing nodded. "Be good," it said. "Peter be good."

"Okay," I said. "Okay."

The thing on the floor closed its eyes and its face went slack, peaceful. I stood there gazing down at it, feeling as if the pain inside me were one that would never go away.

Then I went to the phone to call the police.

33

"Do you know what the worst part of it was?" I asked.

Jack reached out and put a hand on my head and stroked my hair, just once, very soothingly. "Uh-uh," he said. "Tell me."

"That the last time I went to the counseling center, I asked him for a profile of the killer," I said. "And he gave me one, and it turned out to be letter-perfect. The abused child who grew up to be a multiple personality and a sexual sadist." I expelled a long, slow sigh and shook my head. "He was diagnosing himself."

Jack nodded.

It was late Wednesday afternoon, and the two of us were sitting on a bench by the river. To the right of us were the Weld Boathouse and the Larz Anderson Bridge. Behind us the first wave of commuter traffic hummed along Memorial Drive. Across the river the spires of the Business School dreamt against the deepening sky. The surface of the river was like cracked obsidian.

"You never told me you went back to see him a second time," Jack said.

I shrugged. "Slipped my mind, I guess. It was the same afternoon you came to my place to interview my neighbors, remember? And you were acting very mysterious about why you wanted to see them. And you were all charged up about those murders in Indiana. You wouldn't tell me why you were so excited about that, either." I sighed again. "You shoulda told me, Jack."

"Told you what?"

"That you knew Lewis was the killer."

"I didn't *know* that."

"But you suspected it."

"Sure," he said. "That and sixty cents will get you on the subway."

I put my hands in my jacket pockets. "How long did you, um, suspect this?"

He took his hand from my head and made a palms-up gesture with it. "Hard to say. I had a funny feeling about him right from the start."

I looked at him curiously. "Why?"

211

"Oh, I don't know. He was . . ." Jack broke off speaking for a few seconds, as if searching for the appropriate language to convey what was in his mind. "He was—ah, *too* helpful, you know? Too eager to be of assistance."

"He was?" I frowned in some surprise. "That's funny. I got the opposite impression the first time I talked to him. He seemed kind of annoyed that there were cops coming to the center all the time, bugging him about Joan and wanting to know whether she had any homicidal clients." I gave a scornful little laugh. "I thought he was trying to protect the civil rights of all his wackos."

"Well, he probably was," Jack said. "Remember he was Peter Lewis when you saw him there, not Tom Lawrence or whatever. Besides, most people *do* get annoyed or upset after a while if the cops keep coming back and asking them the same questions over and over again. Even if they initially want to help."

"And Lewis did want to help," I said. "At first, anyway."

"Oh, yeah. Too much so."

"I wonder if it actually was Lewis that you talked to some of those times," I mused. "Or maybe Lawrence, and all the alleged *help* he wanted to give you was intended to throw you off the track."

"Maybe," Jack said. "I doubt we'll ever know, though."

I nodded. A woman in a blue pea coat and jeans strolled past us, leading a cocker spaniel puppy on a leash. The pup wanted to stop and sniff every other exposed patch of earth and clump of gray snow. It noticed us on the bench and strained in our direction, tiny tail wagging furiously. The woman tugged at the leash and said, "Come *on*, Sappho," in impatient tones.

"What I would really like to know," I said, "is what put it in your head that Lewis was tied into those murders in Bloomington."

Jack smiled. "That was easy."

"It was?"

"Sure."

"Do tell," I said. I moved closer to him on the bench and he put his arm around me. It was getting terribly cold.

"Okay," he said. "I had been doing a lot of reading, remember, whatever I could get on the subject of sex murders."

"Looking for resemblances," I interrupted, "between something that happened somewhere else and what was happening here, right."

"Yeah. So, anyway, out of everything I checked, the Bloomington business came closest. It was eerie, you know, the similarity?"

"Uh-huh."

"So, for the hell of it, I got in touch with the Indiana state cops and asked them to send me the photographs and diagrams and whatever of the bite marks on those victims."

"And?"

"Identical to the ones on Joan and Sandra and Janice."

"Jesus," I said softly. "When did you get this stuff?"

"Monday."

I thought for a moment. "Okay," I said. "So that definitely established that the Indiana killer and the Cambridge one were the same guy. But how did that point to Lewis?"

Jack smiled again. "He was the only person in the case I could find with an Indiana connection."

I gave him a puzzled look. "What was that? And how'd you find out about it?"

Jack returned my look of puzzlement with a look of amusement. "You were in his office a couple times, Liz. What did he have in there? Think a moment."

I did, for several moments, but to no avail. "I give up," I said. "Tell."

"The diplomas hanging on the wall."

"What about them?"

"Well, where was one of them from?"

My jaw dropped. Jack laughed.

"Indiana," I said. "He graduated from Indiana University. At Blooming-ton."

"Bingo," Jack said. He gave my shoulders a brief squeeze. "Peter Charles Lewis received a master's degree in psychiatric social work from Indiana University three years ago. Just about a month after the murder and rape of the seventh woman in Bloomington."

"Jesus H. Christ," I said, closing my eyes.

"Mmm-hmm."

I blinked. "Was Lewis ever a suspect out there?"

"Nope."

"God. Well"—I put my hand on Jack's knee—"thanks to you, they can close the books on it, finally."

Jack snorted.

"Don't be so modest," I said. "Lewis's bite mark, I take it, is a perfect match for the ones on all ten women?"

"Perfect. Blood type's same as the killer's too. He's it. Plus we got a nice assortment of physical evidence to tie him up."

"Like what?"

"Well"—Jack slouched a little on the bench, gazing out at the river—"for starters, in his apartment, we found the murder weapons."

"Oh?" I raised my eyebrows.

"Yeah. Let's see. A claw hammer—that one seems to have been Sandra—another hammer—probably for Janice." He cleared his throat. "And a cast-iron statue, about eighteen inches high, maybe weighing seven pounds." He gave me a sideways look. "It was of an African woman."

"Joan's," I said. "The Christmas gift from her sister."

"Uh-huh."

"I knew it," I said, slapping my palm against the seat of the bench to emphasize the words. "I knew whoever it was had to have killed those women with something he picked up in their apartments."

Jack nodded. "We also found some surgical gloves. The statue and the hammers were wrapped up in some bloody towels. Which I would imagine he also stole from those women."

"Yuck," I said. "Why?"

"Why the towels?" Jack elevated his left eyebrow. "He used 'em to clean up after himself. After he showered off. He could hardly leave them lying around Joan's or Sandy's or Janice's bathrooms, could he?"

"No," I conceded. "But why in God's name did he save them? And the statue and hammers?"

"Easier and safer than trying to ditch them or throw them away," Jack said. "Also, they made good—ah, trophies."

I gave him a horrified glance. "Trophies," I repeated feelingly. "Of the murders?"

"Yeah."

"That is *disgusting*."

"Disgusting, yes. Unusual, no."

"Huh?"

"Lots of psychopaths have souvenir collections," Jack explained, as if lecturing to a police academy recruit class. "You know Earl Voltz kept a photo album of shots of his victims. Taken with a Polaroid after he killed them."

"Okay," I cut in hastily. "I believe, I believe. Hallelujah, I believe. Nuts dig trophies. Go on."

"Anyway," Jack continued, in his professor voice. "Last Saturday afternoon, when I left your place, I talked to your upstairs neighbor. The Quaalude Kid."

I looked at Jack in astonishment. "Don't tell me he helped you?"

Jack laughed. "Surprisingly, yes. It took a couple visits, and a lot of memory jogging, but finally he came up with some useful information."

"Which was?"

"Well, that he'd seen Joan and Lewis together a few times. I showed him a sketch of Lewis and he was quite definite that that was the man he'd seen in and out of Joan's apartment a couple weeks before she got it."

"When'd you find this out?"

"Monday afternoon."

I brooded. "Same as when you got the stuff from Indiana."

"Yup."

I took a deep breath. "So why didn't you arrest Lewis then?"

"On what grounds? Visiting a co-worker? Getting an M.A. from Indiana University? Neither one's a felony, babe. Not even a misdemeanor, far as I know."

"But . . ."

Jack shook his head patiently. "I had no *proof*, at that point. Sure, I knew the son of a bitch was it. But so what? The Constitution says I can't go around pinching people just because I *know* they did crimes. I have to be able to *prove* they did crimes. Which is as it should be. Though I will admit that it's sort of frustrating on occasion."

I nodded my acceptance of the point. "So what did you do?"

Jack looked slightly uncomfortable. "Put a tail on Lewis."

I practically leaped off the bench. "What?" I screeched. "A tail? What tail? Where the hell was this alleged tail when Lewis was following me home Monday night?"

He looked as if I'd just kicked him in the stomach. "They lost him."

"Swell," I said. "Way to go, cops."

"Believe me," he said. "They've heard about it. At length. From me, from the chief. Mostly from me."

"Okay," I said. I rested my head against his shoulder. He turned and hugged me, quite hard. "That," he said, his voice somewhat muffled, "was the worst part of it, for me."

"Okay," I repeated. "Don't get mushy." I hugged him back, remembering how I'd clung to him like a limpet Monday night, after it was all over, and remembering, too, the expression that had been on his face when he'd burst into my apartment and seen Lewis curled up on the living room floor, crooning wordlessly to himself.

To change the subject, I said, "I know what the connection between Lewis and Joan was. I mean, he told me they'd been having an affair of sorts. But did you ever find out what the deal was with Sandra and Janice?"

"What I figured"—Jack settled back against the bench, but kept one arm around me—"Sandra he picked up in a bar, slept with a few times, and then . . . Janice apparently had met him a few times before—you weren't the only one who went to Inman Square looking for the goods on Joan, cookie—and, I suppose, liked him. Or was attracted to him. She was out Saturday night, and so was he, looking for his next target, and they ran into each other at—" He gave me a wry look. "Guess where?"

That question I could answer. "Jim's Place."

"Uh-huh."

"Ought to be shut down," I muttered.

"Yeah. Well, according to Lewis, or maybe I should say Tom Lawrence, they got to talking and she invited him back to her place for a drink."

"All the while thinking that he was just a nice, attractive guy," I said, almost to myself.

"Yes."

"He told me that he told her he was going to kill her," I continued in the same bodiless voice. "And that's why she put up a fight. In the bedroom."

Jack squeezed my shoulders again, this time comfortingly. "Try not to dwell on that," he said.

I nodded and sighed. "Lewis was taking a big risk, killing her, though, wasn't he? I mean, he hadn't been in her apartment before, had he? He didn't know the lay-out or if there were a weapon available, like he did with Joan and Sandy. And me," I concluded reluctantly.

"Oh, he *had* been in Janice's apartment." Jack paused and scratched the corner of his mouth with his index finger. "Just dropped by one afternoon to bring her some information she wanted about Joan."

I pulled back a bit and stared at Jack, wide-eyed. "Almost the same excuse he used to get into my place, that first time. When he unloaded that box of junk on me that Sunday afternoon."

Jack let out a long breath. "Uh-huh."

"Checking out my living arrangements for future reference," I said bitterly. "In case I turned out to be a whore and he had to beat me to death."

"Maybe."

"Jack?"

"Yeah?"

I moved my head back onto his shoulder. "I still say you should have told me you had bad feelings about Lewis when you started having them. If I'd known I'd never have gone back to see him that second time."

"Yeah, well, maybe I would have told you if you'd bothered to mention ⸜ me that you were going to make a habit of visiting him," Jack replied.

I sighed and shook my head. "Sin of omission. On your part as well as mine, buster."

"Ah, gimme a break," he said. His voice sounded as if he were smiling. "As it is, I tell you much more than I should. I can't tell you everything."

"Even for my own protection?" I said, more sharply than I'd intended. He was silent.

I looked out at the river. The sky was quite dark now, and diamond point reflections of light from the bridge lamps twinkled and shimmered on the surface of the water. A group of student-looking young people, male and female, walked past our bench. They all carried bulging bookbags or knapsacks. On their way back to Quincy House or Dunster or Lowell or Adams or Leverett or Winthrop or Mather for dinner. Over the traffic noise, faintly, I could hear the sound of laughter. Soon the bars would begin to fill.

Peter Lewis, or Tom Lawrence, was doing his eating and drinking tonight in the state hospital at Bridgewater.

God's in his heaven, I thought sardonically, all's right with the world. And then recalled that the man who'd written those words had intended them ironically, too.

I shifted on the bench.

"What is it?" Jack said.

"Another question," I said.

"What?"

"Well, it's sort of gross. But it's something I can't get out of my head."

"Ask," Jack said. "I'm a cop. I can handle gross."

I smiled slightly. "I know. Okay, it's this. What I keep wondering is . . ."

"Yeah?" He encouraged.

"Well"—I breathed deeply of the chilly twilit air—"why did Lewis kill those women and *then* rape them?"

Jack didn't say anything.

"See?" I said. "I told you it was gross."

He shook his head. "It's not that. I was thinking, is all."

"Oh. Well?"

Jack frowned. "Well, I've seen a lot of this sort of stuff. Or heard about it from other cops. And that kind of thing—a postmortem rape, I guess you'd call it—isn't that uncommon."

"But . . . why?"

Jack sucked in his upper lip thoughtfully. "The best I can figure is that the guy who does it is—uh, trying to gain total control of the woman. He's not satisfied just to attack her. He wants *absolute* control over his victim."

217

I nodded.

"And," Jack continued, "he gets it by killing them first. After all, what's more passive and obedient than a corpse?"

I grimaced. "The traditional female role. Carried to its most grotesque extreme."

"If you want to put it that way, yeah."

"You think that's what was motivating Lewis? I mean, Lawrence? The control thing?"

Jack shrugged. "I'm not a shrink. But, yes. I'd say it was possible."

"Have you found out any more about his background?"

It was Jack's turn to make a face. "Yes. Christ." He shook his head slowly.

"What?"

"It's charming." Jack stretched out his legs. "He was born in Cleveland. Who his father was, noboby seems to know. Apparently his mother didn't, either."

"Oh?"

"Well, no. She was a hooker, more or less. Also lived with a succession of guys, outside of her clientele. Had a booze problem, and when she got on a real rip she'd take it out on the kid."

Hurt, I thought, *don't hurt. Peter be good.*

"She wasn't the only one. A couple of the boyfriends thought the kid made a good punching bag, too. Not just that, either." Jack rubbed the side of his face, hard, and closed his eyes as if he were suddenly very tired.

"What?" I said. "What is it?"

The corner of his mouth went down. "Kid was raped by one of them."

"Oh, my God," I said. To my shock, I felt a rush of compassion for Lewis. "That poor little boy."

Please don't hurt no more.

"Anyway," Jack went on, "to make a lousy story short, the mother took off with somebody when Lewis was about ten, and the department of social services finally stepped in, for what that was worth. He got bounced around from one foster family to another till he was about twelve or so, and then got taken in by some couple in Cincinnati."

"And?"

"Well, he seemed to straighten out miraculously. Did real well in high school, graduated with honors, won a scholarship to Stanford."

I nodded. "To study human behavior. Particularly in its more bizarre manifestations."

Jack gave a brief, unamused laugh. "Yeah. Well, he was a model student there, too. Bright, articulate, involved in all sorts of campus activities, sports, the whole bag. No problems anybody ever noticed. Certainly no trouble with women."

"And the whole time," I mused, "the whole time he was being Mr. Perfect Specimen of Young American Manhood, it was festering inside him. All that hate."

"Uh-huh."

"And finally it blew apart," I remarked. "When he got to graduate school." I glanced at Jack. "I wonder what set him off that late in the game?"

"Who knows?" Jack replied. "Could've been anything. Maybe he met a woman who reminded him of his mother."

"Sure," I said. "It was her he was really killing, wasn't it? Killing and controlling."

Mother. Joan. Went away. Whore.

I shivered.

"Cold?" Jack asked.

"Sort of," I said.

"Come on," he said. He stood up and held out a hand to me. "Enough. Let's go get something to eat and drink."

I took his hand and we walked slowly up the embankment to the intersection of Boylston Street and Memorial Drive.

While we were waiting for a break in the traffic so we could cross the street, I said, "He seemed so *nice.*"

Jack looked at me. "Who? Lewis?"

I sighed. "Yeah."

"Aren't they all?" Jack replied. He gave my hand a tug. "Let's go."

We walked across Memorial Drive.

"That's the problem, though," I said, when we got to the other side of the street. "In fact . . ." I stopped and shook my head.

Jack halted beside me. "What?" he said. "What's the problem?"

"Maybe it's just *my* problem," I said. "But . . . you know, Jack, I think I've always taken people at face value. Unless they were blatantly crazy or bad or something. I just assume—God, I'm such a jerk."

He didn't say anything.

"It wasn't just Lewis," I continued. "It was Joan, and Richie Kearns, too."

"So?"

"Well, I guess what's bothering me is that I thought I knew who they were. *What* they were. That I had a least a little sense of them as people.

And"—I gave my head another shake—"I knew nothing about any of them. Not a thing."

We resumed walking up Boylston Street.

"Why does that make you feel bad?" Jack asked as we passed a group of small, brightly lit shops and restaurants.

"It scares me," I said. "It makes me feel sad. As if I have no judgment, no . . . no . . . nothing."

"That's silly," he replied. "How were you supposed to know anything about any of those people? Joan was just an acquaintance. The other two, Kearns and Lewis, were flippos."

"That's just it," I said. "Shouldn't I have spotted that in them?"

"Don't see why," he answered. "No one else did. Till afterward."

I looked at him.

"You're all right," he said. He was smiling.

"But doesn't it worry you?" I persisted. "That it's possible to be so easily fooled by someone's façade?"

"Sure," he said. "But what're you going to do about it? Go around being paranoid about everybody you meet? Assume the worst, all the time? You want to live that way?"

Another group of students swept by us, laughing uproariously at some shared joke. A bus to Allston rumbled down the street. Guitar music was coming from somewhere, probably one of the Harvard houses.

"No," I said quietly.

"So don't worry about it. Now come *on*, for Christ's sake." He smiled again as if to soften the peremptoriness of his tone. "It's cold and I'm hungry. And thirsty."

I opened my mouth, closed it, opened it again, and then sighed.

"Come on," he repeated. He put his arm around me. I pressed against him. He felt, as he always did to me, warm and solid and strong. Real. Probably more real than anyone I'd ever met, or ever would meet. A good person. A good man.

Illusion? If it was, I never wanted to know.

220

If you have enjoyed this book and would like to receive details of other Walker mystery titles, please write to:

Mystery Editor
Walker and Company
720 Fifth Avenue
New York, NY 10019